WHAT OTHERS ARE SAYING ...

"This book is a joy to read! The writing style and wit add dimension in a way that is rarely found in today's reference materials. If someone has considered designing their own airplane and been put off because of complicated formulas, vocabulary and reference style that would bore even an engineer, this will convince them to go ahead and try it. Written with real people in mind and not engineers—and I mean that in a good way. This is a book that will reside along the other favorites on my bookshelf. Carlos really managed to produce a book that will last a long time and become one of the standards for modelers."

Greg Gimlick
Electrics columnist
Model Aviation *magazine*

"This book is definitely needed by anyone getting into R/C or is a veteran flight fanatic! Tons of good info that racks my brain and gets me thinking."

Jamie Burke
Host
AllThingsThatFly.com

"A comprehensive look at what you need to know to design and build your own RC model aircraft. Carlos has distilled his many years of aerodynamic study and model airplane experience into one easy to read book."

Rick Witter
Engineer and Private Pilot

"*RCAdvisor's Model Airplane Design Made Easy* is the ultimate model airplane design book for both beginning and experienced modelers. Everything you need to know is right here with clear, easy-to-understand content that you will refer to again and again. Your understanding of what it takes to design a model airplane will be greatly enhanced by reading this book."

Richard Kline
Inventor
KFm airfoils

"*RCadvisor's Model Airplane Design Made Easy* is a real contribution to the world's literature on the subject. It provides an excellent bridge between full scale aviation and aeromodeling, showing the relationship between the two, for better understanding of the differences and similarities which should be applied for good model performance.

While thorough in detail, the book is also easily readable so that the information is simple to understand. It is a very good combination of theory and practical application. Nicely illustrated, the book is also full of common sense explanations and references to other sources of information."

John Worth
former President and Executive Director of the
Academy of Model Aeronautics and currently Executive
Editor of RC Micro World, *an online monthly maga-*
zine about the smallest and lightest of model aircraft:
www. cloud9rc. com

"If you've ever thought about designing your own models ...

If you've ever thought it would be nice to have alternatives to expensive model building materials ...

If you've ever tried kit-bashing ...

If you've ever looked for a source that could explain the basic principles of aerodynamics clearly and concisely without resorting to complex mathematical formulas ...

Then *RCadvisor's Model Airplane Design Made Easy* is the book for you.

It's a great common-sense guide to the rules-of-thumb of aerodynamics and aircraft design."

Rocky S. Stone
38 years of modeling experience

"Carlos Reyes personally leads the reader through some basic aerodynamics, materials considerations, electric power system planning and a practical application of theory as it is applied to a finished flying model. The background history of various types of aircraft shows the development of aviation and how it relates to the models that we build and fly today, as well as how models have influenced general aviation. It is always exciting to find some "new to me" concepts and theories, and there were several in this well-written narrative."

Ken Myers
Editor
Ampeer *electric flight newsletter*

"No matter how long you've been aeromodelling, or what your interests are in our great hobby, the greatest thrill of all is standing behind a unique model that you've designed and built yourself, from a blank sheet of paper—or even a blank CAD file—and preparing to make that first take off.

So sit yourself down in a comfy chair, read *RCadvisor's Model Airplane Design Made Easy* and set off on aeromodelling's greatest adventure.

Let Carlos Reyes—an aeromodeller of long standing and great talent—take you through the mysteries of how to arrive at the point that every lover of model aircraft should experience."

Dereck Woodward
aeromodeller, designer and
magazine writer for the past fifty years

RCADVISOR'S
MODEL AIRPLANE DESIGN
MADE EASY

The Simple Guide to
Designing R/C Model Aircraft
or
Build Your Own
Radio Control Flying Model Plane

Carlos Reyes
www.RCadvisor.com founder

RCadvisor.com
Albuquerque, New Mexico

Published by:
RCadvisor.com
2200 Elizabeth St NE
Albuquerque, NM 87112-3037
1-505-206-1569
carlos@rcadvisor.com

ISBN 978-0-9822613-2-3

Library of Congress Control Number: 2009900547
Library of Congress subject headings:
Airplanes—Models—Design and construction.
Airplanes—Models—Aerodynamics.
Airplanes—Models—Radio control.

Cover design by Tammy Crespin. Book design by Carlos Reyes. Typeset using the amazing LaTeX system.

This paper meets the requirements of ANSI/NISO Z39.48-1992 (Permanence of Paper).

Version 1.0

To Tammy and Autumn,
the ladies in my life.

Summary Table of Contents

Contents

List of Figures

List of Tables

List of Equations

Preface

"If we are what we eat, then some pilots need to eat more chicken."

Anonymous

I'm a licensed full-size glider pilot with hundreds of hours of experience. I enjoyed flying these majestic birds immensely, but I haven't done so for about four years now and I don't regret leaving the sport. How come? I'm having a ton of fun with what I'm doing now.

I used to belong to a large soaring club that has been around for over fifty years. One of my fellow club members had actually built his own fiberglass glider. As I recall, it had taken him about five years of full-time work. Half way through he developed an epoxy allergy, so his retired wife had to finish the fiberglass work for him. The finished glider looked and flew beautifully, but putting it together was an ordeal that he did not wish to repeat.

Designing model airplanes is fun. They provide an incredible creative outlet, unmatched in full-size aviation. A very dedicated individual could perhaps design, build and test fly one full-size airplane per decade and it would cost many thousands of dollars. On the other hand, a model airplane can be designed and built in one day for very little money.

I founded RCadvisor[1] out of my love for aviation in general and model airplanes in particular. With thousands of registered website members, I see first hand the challenges faced by modelers every day. Putting together an *efficient* power system for a model airplane is not easy. Designing your own original model airplane is not easy to do well. Today, RCadvisor's on-line

---

[1] www. RCadvisor. com

calculator helps you with the first task. This book helps you with the second one.

Overview of the book

This book consists of a broad overview of a series of topics important to model airplane design. A lot of theory is covered, but always with an eye strictly on its practical application.

Appendices contain various resources that I've found useful.

I also enjoy flying model helicopters (see Figure 0.1 on the facing page), but they, unfortunately, do not lend themselves easily to homegrown designs. They will not be discussed directly, though much of the book is relevant to understanding how they fly.

The chapters in the book follow a logical progression. You may have difficulty understanding the material in a later chapter if you are unfamiliar with the subjects covered earlier on.

A lot of ground is covered very quickly. Don't let the short length of some sections trick you into believing that they are not important and can be skipped. Everything in the book is here for a reason, and it is often because the information is important and it is difficult to find elsewhere.

At the same time, I gloss over information readers may already be familiar with or that a quick Internet search will yield dozens of explanations. A favorite resource of mine is Wikipedia[2], usually providing just the right level of detail.

Think of the book as a set of recipes. Regardless of the specific goals for your design, you will find much information that can be leveraged and applied successfully. At the very least, my hope is to get the reader to consider all of these dimensions of their design.

The dual goals of targetting a global audience and staying away from the clutter of units of measure proved to be a challenge. Where no units are specified, it is imperative to use a *consistent* set of units. If you decide to mix

---

[2] `www.wikipedia.org`

Figure 0.1. Model helicopter
Much of the book applies directly to model helicopters.

together centimeters and inches, you are on your own. Angles are always in degrees unless specified otherwise.

Dimensionless quantities by definition have no units associated with them. Sometimes all the units of the values they are derived from do not entirely cancel out. That is fine as long as the units were consistent with each other to begin with.

Disclaimers

This book is designed to provide information on designing, building and flying model aircraft. It is sold with the understanding that the publisher and author are not involved in rendering professional services. If expert assistance is required, the services of a competent professional should be sought.

It is not the purpose of this book to reprint all the information that is otherwise available, but instead to complement, amplify and supplement other information sources.

Trademarked names are used throughout this book. We are using the names only in an editorial fashion. The usage is to the benefit of the trademark owners and there is no intention to infringe on their legal rights.

Every effort has been made to make this book as complete and accurate as possible. However, I am not perfect. This book may contain both typographical and content errors.

The purpose of this book is to educate and entertain. The author and RCadvisor.com shall have neither liability nor responsibility to any person or entity with respect to any loss or damage caused, or alleged to have been caused, directly or indirectly, by the information contained in this book.

Acknowledgments

I have not attempted to cite in the text all the authorities and sources consulted in the preparation of this book. To do so would require more space than is available.

When I decided to write this book, I figured I would be the only person that would read it all before it's release. Imagine my delight and dismay when most of the recipients of early rough drafts proceeded to read it cover to cover! In no particular order, the reviewers were Rocky Stone, Dereck Woodward, Greg Gimlick, Jamie Burke, John Worth, Ken Myers, Richard Kline, Rick Witter, Edgar Reyes, and Tammy Crespin. The book is much improved because of their many thoughtful comments. Thank you.

1. Fluid Dynamics Boot Camp

1.1. Introduction

A flight instructor named Al Santilli used to live near me, here in Albuquerque, New Mexico. He died in 2007 at the age of 91. Why am I telling you about him? He was the 243rd private pilot licensed in the United States. His flight instructor was Orville Wright, the co-inventor of the first successful powered airplane.

The history of manned flight is barely a hundred years old. Aerodynamics is a fairly new science. There is much that we understand, but there are also many mysteries waiting to be solved. I have a shelf full of aerodynamics books which I'm constantly consulting. Several of these books contain over 1,000 pages. The purpose of this chapter is not to try and summarize everything that I've learned about this important subject. Instead, I want to give you a flavor of the aerodynamic challenges faced by flying model airplanes. Along the way I'll share some rules of thumb that I've found useful and you might want to apply to your own designs.

The concepts explained in this chapter are critical to understanding how airfoils, propellers, and wings work. It is impossible to make rational design decisions without at least a basic understanding of the aerodynamics involved. Model airplanes face unique aerodynamic challenges because of their small sizes and slow speeds, making this basic knowledge doubly important.

1.2. Viscosity

A fluid is a substance that continually deforms (in other words, flows) when a shear force is applied. All liquids and all gases are fluids. Viscosity is a measure of the resistance of a fluid to be deformed. Thick fluids like vegetable oil have higher viscosity than water, a relatively thin fluid. Water is about 50 times more viscous than air.

Sometimes it can be hard to tell whether a substance is a solid or a fluid. Pitch, a black substance also known as resin or bitumen, is an extremely viscous fluid. To the naked eye it appears to be a solid, shattering when struck with a hammer. It is estimated to be 100 billion times more viscous than water. A pitch drop experiment in Australia has only counted eight drops since the experiment started in 1930.

1.3. Viscous and Inviscid Flows

There are some very strange fluids that have zero viscosity. Liquid helium is one of them. When put inside a sealed container, it flows to cover the entire surface of the container.

When a fluid flows, there are two forces at play. Inertia seeks to keep the fluid moving, while viscosity forces it to slow down. Depending upon the speed of the fluid, one or the other force can dominate. When moving very quickly, inertia takes over and the effects due to viscosity can usually be ignored. This is what's called an inviscid flow. A viscous flow is when both forces need to be taken into account.

1.4. Lift

The lift generated by a wing is the result of reduced air pressure over it. When a fluid such as air is forced to travel a longer distance over a curved surface, it speeds up and, in turn, its pressure drops. This is due to the famous Bernoulli theorem, formulated by Daniel Bernoulli in 1738.

Lift is generated even if the air is traveling over a flat surface. When it is tilted upwards, it forces the air that goes over the top to travel a farther distance. Experiments have proven that the air going over the top actually reaches the trailing edge of the wing first.

About two-thirds of the lift is generated by the lower pressure over the top surface. The other third is due to the increased pressure over the bottom. It's the flip side of the coin of the Bernoulli theorem: the air slows down as it goes by the bottom, so the pressure increases.

There is an alternative explanation of lift that you may come across. It states that lift is due to a mass of air being deflected downwards. This is the old action-reaction principle at play, also known as Isaac Newton's Third Law of Motion. It is not a bad way of looking at the phenomenon, but it is less useful when doing the computations than the pressure differential explanation.

1.5. Drag

Drag is the villain in aerodynamics. It is the force that you are always trying to minimize but can never get rid of. Yeah, what a drag!

1.5.1. Skin Friction Drag

When an object moves through the air, it slows down the air molecules that touch it. This slowing down effect is skin friction drag. There is not a lot that you can do about it, except for the obvious design changes:

- Use a smaller wing

- Reduce the size of the fuselage

- Use a flying wing

- Use a smooth surface

1.5.2. Separation Drag

As air flows around an object, it slows down as it enters a region of increasing pressure. This is the so-called adverse pressure gradient and is due again to Bernoulli's theorem. As it slows down, it loses momentum or inertia. At some point it loses so much momentum that it pulls away from the surface contour it was following. The drag force that results is the so-called separation or form drag.

Another term you might come across is parasitic drag, which is the combination of form (separation), skin friction, and interference drag. Interference drag is a type of form drag.

Separation drag has been the primary focus in drag reduction design work for airplanes almost since their invention. Early airplanes all used external wire bracing. These wires were round in cross section, generating a huge amount of separation drag (see Figure 1.1 on the next page). Properly streamlined into a teardrop shape, their drag would have been ten times smaller. That is a big difference! If you cannot easily streamline or get rid of the wires, put them at an angle to the airstream (see Table 1.1 on the facing page). If you can get the wires to only have an angle of 30 degrees to the airflow, the drag will be reduced to 50% of the original drag.

Even in a properly streamlined shape, about 15 percent of the drag experienced will be separation drag, the rest being skin friction drag.

As it flies through the air, an airplane is never perfectly aligned with the airflow. Even if the movements are too small to see, it is always getting buffeted around. Any part of the airplane that is not nicely rounded, like a squared-off wingtip, will experience separation drag when the surface is turned away from the airstream, even if it is at a small angle.

1.5.3. Induced Drag

As an airplane flies more slowly, the entire airplane has to tilt up so that the wing can continue to generate the same amount of lift. But now the top of the wing is pointing away from the direction in which you are flying. This means that some of the lift being produced is actually in the direction

Figure 1.1. Bristol Boxkite

A very early airplane design from 1910. Note the large number of exposed wires. The drag from the wires must have been enormous!

Angle (°)	Drag (%)
90	100
80	98
70	94
60	87
50	77
45	71
40	64
30	50
20	34
10	17
0	0

Table 1.1. Air drag on exposed wire

Keep the angle to 20 degrees or less.

opposite from which the airplane is traveling. This backward facing lift force is called induced drag. Induced drag is the drag that is created, or induced, in the process of generating lift with a wing. It is proportional to the lift coefficient squared.

As the airplane flies more slowly, the induced drag gets much bigger. A common fallacy is that the minimum energy required to fly occurs right before the stall. This is simply not true due to the greatly increased induced drag at this speed. In fact, to fly just above the stall speed requires a great deal of power to counteract the induced drag.

1.6. Laminar Flow

Laminar flow is when a fluid such as air smoothly moves in a straight line. There is little friction and loss of energy as the mass of air moves across. It's relatively easy to run accurate computer simulations that predict the behavior of laminar flows. Fluid flows *always* start out as laminar.

1.7. Separation Bubbles

Since laminar flows are low energy flows, they have trouble working their way around obstacles. As the flow goes around an obstacle, it slows down. A fluid slows down when the pressure on the fluid increases. When the velocity goes down to zero, a phenomenon called *separation* comes into play. This means that the fluid is no longer flowing smoothly in the same direction but has actually reversed direction. All of this happens a very small distance from the surface (see Figure 1.2 on the next page).

A separation bubble over a wing dramatically decreases the lift it generates and dramatically increases the separation drag. How much? It depends, but half the lift and five times the drag is not unusual. Separation bubbles are always bad news and airplane designers are always struggling to eliminate them or at least minimize their size.

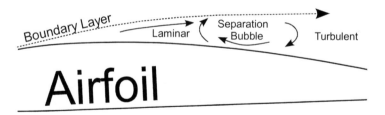

Figure 1.2. Transition to turbulent flow
Note the laminar separation bubble. Vertical scale greatly exaggerated.

Note that laminar flow is not a prerequisite for a separation bubble to form. In fact, it is not uncommon for a series of small separation bubbles to form as the air moves past an object. An airplane is said to stall when a separation bubble over its wing grows large. A separation bubble that forms in a laminar flow is especially important because it usually signals the transition to turbulent flow.

1.8. Chaos Theory

Understanding turbulent flows requires some knowledge of chaos theory. But first, a story.

I took an elective in college once. It was the first time the class was being offered, and for all I know it was the last. The professor was totally disorganized. All I learned in that class was from the book, since the lessons were useless. Right before the midterm, he confessed to us that he usually stayed up late right before a big exam, just like the students. No, not studying but putting the exam together! One day a visiting professor happened to walk down the hallway while the class was in session. My teacher grabbed him and did everything he could to get the poor sap to teach the class for him. The name of the class? Appropriately enough, Chaos Theory.

The popular name for chaos theory is the butterfly effect, first used in a short story by Ray Bradbury in 1952. It is the idea that a small change in initial conditions of a system can have a large effect eventually.

These systems are still fully deterministic, meaning that randomness plays no role in them. This definition is at odds with the common usage of the word 'chaos', which implies that the system is fully random. Deterministic chaotic systems may appear to be random or at least it is very hard to predict their behavior. A perfect example is the weather. Chaos theory has been used to prove that weather forecasting cannot ever be done accurately for periods that are longer than a week into the future.

Chaotic systems are predictable to some degree. The usual approach is to run multiple computer simulations and to take the average of all the results obtained.

1.9. Turbulent Flow

Turbulent fluid flows are rough and chaotic. They are very hard to understand and predict. A laminar flow will turn turbulent in the middle of a separation bubble or when the ripples in the fluid gain inertia and grow out of control. Once the flow turns turbulent, it will normally continue to stay that way.

Turbulent flows follow the rules of deterministic chaos. It is really hard to make an accurate prediction about the transition from a laminar to a turbulent flow region. Carefully controlled wind tunnel tests, even within the same wind tunnel, always yield slightly different answers. Different computer simulation programs, no matter how sophisticated, always yield slightly different results, too. It is not because of any inherent flaws in the construction of the wind tunnels or computer programs. It is simply because of the nature of the problem.

Drag from a turbulent flow is about twice as much as from a laminar flow. Based on this, you would expect that the goal in an airplane design would be to maintain laminar flow as long as possible. Well, it's actually more complicated than that. You see, laminar flows are prone to creating separation bubbles. A turbulent flow, since it's high energy, will resist separation much more by being able to follow the contours of an object a lot more easily. Shortly, in section 1.12 on page 39, I'll describe a way to encourage the early transition to a turbulent flow.

Separation bubbles are bad all around. Lots of drag, lots of lost lift. Avoid them at all costs.

1.10. Dimensionless Numbers

A dimensionless number is a pure quantity without any physical units associated with it. There are about fifty different dimensionless numbers that are used to characterize fluid flows. For two flows to be considered similar, all of these numbers must match. In practice most of these numbers are ignored in order to simplify the comparison process. By far the two most important dimensionless numbers are the Reynolds and Mach numbers. Two other numbers you might come across are the Euler (used to predict energy losses in the flow) and Froude (useful in predicting air turbulence) numbers.

1.10.1. Reynolds Number

Below a certain speed, fluids like air tend to flow smoothly in laminar flows. When disturbed, the ripples created are quickly quieted down. As their speed increases, fluids are less able to overcome disturbances in their flow. Above a certain speed, any disturbance in the flow will tend to grow in size until the entire flow becomes turbulent. What is really happening is that at low flow speeds, the viscosity of the fluid is enough to keep the fluid particles moving smoothly. At higher speeds, the inertia of the particles is so high that their energy overcomes the tendency for them to stick together.

The ratio of inertial forces to viscous forces is called the Reynolds number. Regardless of which fluid we are talking about, below a Reynolds number of 2,320 the disturbances or eddies will always be smoothed out. Above that number, there are many factors that determine whether the flow will stay laminar or turn turbulent. In fact, it is not unusual for a flow to stay laminar at a Reynolds number of 60,000, assuming that the surface is smooth and straight enough. The Reynolds number when the flow turns turbulent for that given surface is the so-called *critical Reynolds number*. In air, a flow over a smooth airfoil might turn turbulent at a Reynolds number between 50,000 and 70,000. Below that, it's probably laminar. Above that, it's probably turbulent. In between, flip a coin.

When an object moves through the air, it's size and velocity can be used to estimate the Reynolds number in effect:

$$Reynolds Number_{English} \approx feet * \frac{mi}{h} * 10,000 \qquad (1.1)$$

$$Reynolds Number_{metric} \approx meters * \frac{m}{s} * 70,000 \qquad (1.2)$$

You may be asking yourself, when an air molecule is passing by an object, how does it know how big that object is? Let's say an air molecule just hit the windshield of your car as it drives down the road. Whether it turns turbulent or not depends on the Reynolds number, which in turn depends on the size of the object. But it doesn't know the size of your car, since the car is still in the process of driving by that air molecule. The answer is the air molecule's behavior depends only on the *local Reynolds number*, which is the size of the object as measured from the front end up until where the air molecule is at that moment. As far as the air molecule is concerned, the only object size that counts is that part of the object which it has passed by. As it continues to move, the local Reynolds number continues to increase until it reaches the rear end of the object. At that point the local Reynolds number is the same as the full object's Reynolds number.

1.10.2. Mach Number

The Mach number is the speed of an object relative to the speed of sound. Sound travels about five times faster through water, so this is not something that boats have to worry about. It is a dimensionless quantity expressed as a fraction of the speed of sound. The speed of sound is only affected by temperature, not altitude.

As the speed of an object increases, it becomes harder and harder for the air molecules to move out of the way. The air starts getting compressed as it gets pushed out of the way. Below Mach 0.3, there is less than a 5% difference in the results when Mach effects are taken into account. For all practical purposes, the Mach number can be ignored when the airspeed is less than 200 $\frac{mi}{h}$ (100 $\frac{m}{s}$). Therefore, Mach effects might be a problem with model airplane propellers but not with model airplane wings, which we will discuss later.

1.11. Boundary Layer

Air has viscosity. This means that there is resistance that slows it down as it moves past objects.

In 1904 Ludwig Prandtl published a paper at the Third International Mathematical Congress. In this paper he theorized that the velocity of a moving fluid (such as air) right at a surface was zero. He further theorized that the effect of this friction was limited to a thin layer right above the surface called the boundary layer. In other words, he said that the flow need only be viewed as viscous within the boundary layer. Beyond the boundary layer, the calculations could be simplified by assuming that the flow was inviscid. For the first time in history, Prandtl's paper simplified enough the formulas of fluid motion that they could finally be solved. He is called by many the father of aerodynamics, and should have earned the Nobel prize for his paper.

Even after the flow in the boundary layer has turned turbulent, there is always a portion of the boundary layer, called the sub-boundary layer, that is always laminar.

$$LaminarBLThickness_{English} = \frac{5.0 * feet}{\sqrt{LocalReynoldsNumber}} \quad (1.3)$$

$$LaminarBLThickness_{metric} = \frac{5.0 * meters}{\sqrt{LocalReynoldsNumber}} \quad (1.4)$$

$$TurbulentBLThickness_{English} = \frac{0.37 * feet}{\sqrt[5]{LocalReynoldsNumber}}$$
$$(1.5)$$

$$TurbulentBLThickness_{metric} = \frac{0.37 * meters}{\sqrt[5]{LocalReynoldsNumber}}$$
$$(1.6)$$

Just how thick is this boundary layer that we keep talking about? Very thin. Let's say we have a 9 inch (23 centimeter) chord wing (the chord of a wing is the distance from the leading edge to the trailing edge) on a model airplane that is flying at 30 mi/h (13.4 m/s). Assume that laminar flow continues for 3 inches (7.6 centimeters) back from the leading edge. The boundary layer thickness at this point will be 0.056 inches (1.4 millimeters). Assume now that the flow turns turbulent at this point. We cannot just calculate the turbulent boundary layer thickness, since we are not starting at the leading edge. We have to start with the thickness of the boundary layer where the laminar flow stops and use that as the starting point for turbulent computation. The boundary layer thickness 6 inches (15 centimeters) back from the leading edge will be 0.17 inches (4.3 millimeters) thick. If it had remained laminar, it would just be 0.077 inches (2.0 millimeters) thick.

The faster the airplane flies, the more slowly the boundary layer grows. Model airplanes have relatively large boundary layer thicknesses as compared to full-size airplanes. Since this is where turbulence and separation bubbles occur (the bad guys), they have a harder time generating lift efficiently.

If the flow velocity right at the surface is zero, does that mean that there is a mass of air that the airplane is bringing along for the ride, adding to the weight of the airplane? Yes! This extra mass is normally ignored for airplanes, being significant only for large vehicles such as dirigibles. A rule of thumb is to multiply 2.5% of the total aircraft volume (not surface area!) times the air density. Air has a density of about 0.075 pounds/foot³ (1.2 kg/meter³), so it is just not much added weight for your typical model airplane.

1.12. Micro Vortex Generators

Since separation bubbles are so bad, is there a way to trigger a transition directly to turbulent flow, bypassing the loss of lift associated with bubbles? Yes. That is the job of turbulators and other boundary layer control devices.

The dimples on a golf ball act like little vortex generators (see Section 1.14 on page 42). Without them, the ball would develop a large separation bubble with lots of drag. With the dimples, early transition to turbulent flow occurs and there is a lot less drag. The result is that the golf ball flies much farther with the dimples.

Most of the time these devices are there to help lower the stall speed. That is when you are more likely to get separation bubbles. Some full-size airplanes also use them to control the separation drag, such as the junction of the wing and fuselage. That is an advanced usage that has little practical value in a model airplane.

Don't make the mistake of using these as a band-aid for a poorly designed airfoil. A properly shaped airfoil experiencing laminar flow will always have lower drag than a poorly shaped airfoil with turbulators.

A common problem with flow control devices for lowering the stall speed is that they increase the drag at speeds where they are not needed, such as at cruise. One of the better solutions are micro vortex generators, which lie entirely within the boundary layer. Properly sized and located, they have been shown to reduce drag by as much as 35% and they have a minimal effect at cruise speeds. Unfortunately, that is easier said than done. Adding vortex control devices is a bit of a black art, but hopefully the guidelines in this section will provide you with an effective starting point.

A very effective type of micro vortex generator is the separated counter-rotating vane. Let the maximum height of the device be 20% the height of the boundary layer at its rearmost position. Make the length of each leg be 10 times this height. Each leg is a triangular piece that starts at zero height at the front. The angle between the legs is 80 degrees. Put a gap one device height wide at the tallest end of the arrow. You end up with what looks like an arrow pointing towards the trailing edge of the wing. Position a series of these wedges 12 device heights apart (see Figure 1.3 on the facing page).

How far back from the leading should these be located? That is a difficult question to answer. On the one hand, they need to be placed ahead of the onset of the turbulent flow. Once the flow turns turbulent, you may have already developed a separation bubble. On the other hand, this transition point changes position depending on the flying speed. A good starting point is to place the micro vortex generator at a local Reynolds number of 30,000 when the airplane is flying close to the stall speed.

1.13. Low Reynolds Numbers

At Reynolds numbers of less than 100,000 flows can be very problematic with frequent separation bubbles.

At Reynolds numbers from 10,000 to 30,000 the goal is to maintain laminar flow as long as possible. If a separation bubble develops, it will not reattach. Boundary layer control devices (turbulators and the like) are simply not effective. Once the flow stops being laminar, it'll remain separated and it won't transition into a turbulent flow.

At 50,000 and higher you have a chance at a separation bubble transitioning to turbulent flow. Use boundary layer control devices to encourage this.

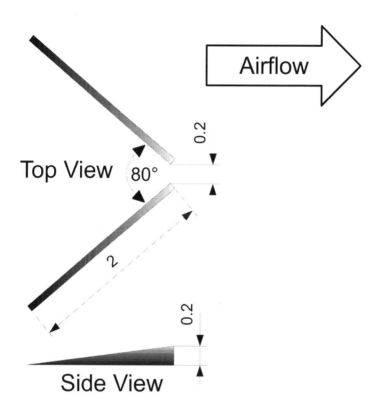

Figure 1.3. Micro vortex generator
This one is called a separated counter-rotating vane. The units are the fraction of the boundary layer height (0.2 = 20%).

1.14. Golf Balls

Well, it's time I cut to the chase and finally get to the reason why you bought this book in the first place—to learn why golf balls have dimples.

Seriously, although this is a little bit of a tangent (golf balls do fly, don't they?), the discussion will be very helpful in tying everything we've learned together.

In 1845 the first completely smooth golf ball flew. It was soon discovered that it did not fly as far as its predecessor which had a rough surface. Why, oh why?

The critical Reynolds number is higher for a smooth surface than for a rough surface. This means that the airflow over a smooth golf ball will stay laminar longer than for a rough ball.

A golf ball flies at a Reynolds number of about 100,000. That is high enough to guarantee a transition to turbulent flow, but not high enough to guarantee that it will occur near the front of the ball. Much higher or lower than this Reynolds number, and dimples would have little effect.

Similar to an airfoil, when the air hits the front of the ball it starts speeding up and it starts to drop in pressure. As soon as the air is past the thickest part of the ball (the middle), it starts to slow down and once again increase in pressure. This is called an adverse pressure gradient and easily leads to separation and turbulent flow (see Figure 1.2 on page 33).

Since balls are fat and not very streamlined, a laminar flow will turn turbulent as soon as it's past the middle of a smooth ball and enters the adverse pressure gradient on the backside.

Dimples on a golf ball encourage the early transition to a turbulent flow. This means that the flow will be fully turbulent by the time it enters the adverse pressure gradient. Turbulent flows have more energy and can follow the contour of an object better.

With an object as round as a ball, a separation bubble is inevitable. But the early transition to turbulent flow allows this separation bubble to be much smaller than with laminar flow. The much smaller separation bubble produces much less drag.

The dimples do increase the skin friction drag. But because of the relatively slow speeds at which golf balls travel (150 miles/hour or 70 m/s), the increased skin friction drag is much less than the reduction in separation drag. In fact, with the dimples, the total drag is cut in half. That's a lot!

Backspin on a golf ball means that the top surface moves in the same direction as the air. With the ball spinning this way, the air over the top surface will speed up and the air going under the bottom will slow down. The Bernoulli principle comes into play again and the ball will produce lift. This is called the Magnus effect and is much more pronounced when the ball has dimples. This is a secondary effect to the reduction in total drag described above.

2. Airfoils

Airfoils are overrated. I don't mean to say that they are no good, but that way too much emphasis is placed on them in an airplane design (both models and full-size). This is because it's easy to analyze an airfoil in isolation, they are easily interchangeable within an airplane design, and large libraries of proven airfoils are readily available.

> "I once stood and listened to a guy at a NEAT Fair explain to Keith Shaw how his show plane would fly so much better if he used a better airfoil. Keith told him why he flew with the airfoil that he did, but the guy just continued to go on. Finally he asked Keith why he refused to listen to reason. Keith, as only Keith can, replied 'because my plane flies so well the way it is!'"
>
> *Greg Gimlick*

Sometimes using the right airfoil can give you a big advantage. After the success of the Wright brothers, many serious academic researchers turned their attention to the problem of flight. The leading aerodynamicist at the time was Ludwig Prandtl in Germany. But the outbreak of World War I in 1914 delayed the spread of his ideas.

An airplane like the British Sopwith Camel (see Figure 2.1 on page 47) from 1916 represents the older school of thought. It had many drag producing exposed wires, a very low aspect ratio of 4.11 (aspect ratio is the wingspan divided by the average wing width), and very thin wings. The thin wing airfoils were thought to be superior because of a lack of understanding of Reynolds number effects. At the very low Reynolds numbers that the testing was done, thin airfoils work better. But they were inferior to thicker airfoils at the speeds these airplanes flew at.

The German Fokker D-VII (see Figure 2.2 on page 48) from 1917 represents an entirely new approach to airplane design. It had a lot fewer exposed wires than the Camel, a higher aspect ratio of 4.7, and an airfoil about twice as thick. This airfoil produced much less drag and more lift than thin airfoils. At the end of the war, the Allies only demanded that one airplane type be handed over: the feared D-VII. With its better climb rate, more maneuverability, and excellent handling qualities, this was the best fighter of the war.

Sometimes picking the wrong airfoil can cause serious problems, but these cases are relatively rare. Burt Rutan, when designing the VariEze canard homebuilt (see Figure 5.8 on page 102), needed an airfoil for the canard surface. There were not too many airfoils that had been tested down to the 675,000 Reynolds number that he needed. He also didn't have the money or time to conduct his own wind tunnel testing. He chose the GU25-5(11)8 airfoil, designed at Glasgow University and tested down to a Reynolds number of 500,000. Unfortunately, the problem was that this airfoil had been designed for conducting research in human powered flight in the 1960s. This was a very specialized application. Being able to fly while it was raining or when covered with bugs was simply not one of the original design requirements. This oversight on Rutan's part came back to haunt him when the VariEze canard surface lost much of its ability to create lift during a rain storm. Eventually Rutan switched to the Roncz R1145M3 airfoil, which was much more resistant to surface contamination.

When the airfoil thickness is referred to, it means the maximum airfoil thickness. This is the maximum distance between the upper surface and the lower surface. Camber is the maximum distance between the chord line and the mean camber line (see Figure 2.3 on page 49). Both of these are usually given as percentages of the chord size. The mean camber line is the halfway point between the upper surface and the lower surface.

Figure 2.1. Sopwith Camel
Due to a lack of understanding of Reynolds number effects, they made the wings way too thin.

Figure 2.2. Fokker D-VII
Used a thick airfoil, as dictated by the best aerodynamic research at the time.

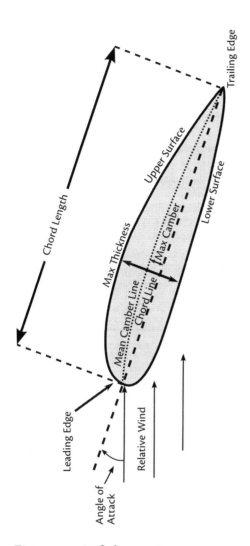

Figure 2.3. Airfoil geometry

2.1. Key Performance Characteristics

There are three characteristics of airfoils that you should be familiar with. No airfoil can be good at all three. The best hope an airfoil designer has is to optimize one of these qualities and have average performance in the other two. If I were putting together a catalog of all airfoils, these are the three primary categories I would divide them into.

Besides these three, another performance characteristic you might come across is the pitching moment or moment coefficient. This is the tendency of the airfoil to change its angle of attack. Most airfoils have a negative moment coefficient, meaning that they tend to pitch down. Generally speaking the more camber, the more negative the pitching moment. As a quick check, look at the angle of the trailing edge. The more it points down, the more negative the moment coefficient.

Airfoils with negative pitching moments are normally used because they are very good at producing lift efficiently, not because they are required for stability. The center of gravity and the elevator work together to balance out the pitching force, if any. For an airplane to be statically stable, the pitching moment of the entire airplane must become more negative as the angle of attack increases, and vice versa. This is exactly the job of the horizontal stabilizer. Flying wings and canards work similarly.

A wing with plastic film covering that sags in between the ribs will of course exhibit behavior that is a combination of the various airfoil thicknesses. Unfortunately, it may not be easy to correctly guess what that behavior might be.

Finally, keep in mind that the Reynolds number affects all of these values. Needless to say, the lower the Reynolds number the worse the performance characteristics become.

2.1.1. Minimum Drag Coefficient

This is the minimum drag of the airfoil. It's usually very close to the zero lift angle. It's a primary factor in determining the maximum speed of the airplane. If your model needs to fly fast, think thin thoughts. The thinner the airfoil, the lower the zero lift drag. Airfoil camber (bend) has some effect on this value.

The angle of attack for minimum drag is usually between -5 and 0 degrees. This too changes with the Reynolds number.

2.1.2. Maximum Lift Coefficient

The highest amount of lift that the airfoil can produce. For most airfoils this is very close to the stall (some airfoils mush along without stalling). This helps determine the landing and take-off airspeeds—the higher the maximum lift coefficient, the lower the stalling speed. Airfoils that are about 12% thick (the thickness is measured as a percentage of the chord length) usually produce the highest lift coefficients. Increasing airfoil camber normally increases this value.

Thin airfoils and those with sharp leading edges tend to have bad stall characteristics. This means that the wing suddenly stops producing lift and the model falls out of the sky. You do not want one of these airfoils if the design is intended to be a trainer, for example.

2.1.3. Maximum Lift to Drag Ratio

The efficiency of the airfoil. The maximum is usually at angles of attack of 2 to 5 degrees. It can be used to predict the endurance and range of the airplane. This value does not change with altitude, but at higher altitudes it is reached at higher speeds. It is also not affected by wing loading, requiring a higher speed to reach it with more weight. The best L/D ratio for a given airfoil shape is usually obtained by making it about 12% thick.

The design lift coefficient of a wing is the lift coefficient at cruise speed. Since this is where the airplane is expected to spend most of its time, a value is chosen that has a lift to drag ratio near the maximum. Note that the lift coefficient of a wing is usually very close to the lift coefficient of the airfoil it uses.

You can use (2.1) to compute the required lift coefficient. The density of the standard atmosphere at sea level is 0.07647 lb/ft³ (1.225 kg/m³). Keep your units straight when using this formula!

$$liftCoefficient = \frac{2 * modelWeight}{airspeed^2 * wingArea * airDensity} \tag{2.1}$$

2.2. Recommendations

In 1932 NACA (the predecessor of NASA) created a family of airfoils and tested them in a wind tunnel. The most famous of these airfoils is the NACA 2412, widely used to this day. Most Cessna single engine airplanes use it. It is very similar to the Clark Y airfoil which preceded it and was already very popular.

In 1977 NASA set out to improve this workhorse of aviation. They initially labelled it the GA(W)-2, which means General Aviation (Whitcomb)-number two. Not happy with one cryptic name, it was later renamed to LS(1)-0413 which means low-speed (1st series), design lift coefficient of 0.4, and thickness of 13%.

If you are looking for a general purpose, jack-of-all-trades, all-around nice kind of guy airfoil, my strong recommendation is the NASA LS(1)-0413 airfoil (see Figure 2.4).

Figure 2.4. NASA LS(1)-0413 airfoil

This airfoil has it all, as far as I'm concerned. Outstanding maximum lift coefficient, excellent lift to drag ratio, and good zero lift drag. It has a very gentle stall and is very resistant to errors in manufacture or bugs/dirt on the leading edge. It is thick enough to allow a nice thick wing spar.

The king (2412) is dead. Long live the king!

2.2.1. Low Reynolds Numbers

At Reynolds numbers of less than 100,000 the rules change and you have to treat the airflow gingerly to avoid separation. A thick airfoil like the NASA LS(1)-0413 just doesn't work. Airfoils should be no more than 6% thick, have 5% or less of camber, and have maximum thickness at 25% of the chord. A camber of 5% will give you the best maximum lift, a camber of 3% will give you the best lift/drag ratio.

Two good examples of airfoils like this are the Göttingen 397 (see Figure 2.5 on the following page) and the Eppler E71 (see Figure 2.6 on the next page). The Göttingen has maximum thickness of 5.1%, maximum camber of 3.9% and position of maximum thickness at 29% of the chord. The Eppler has maximum thickness of 5.2%, maximum camber of 4.6% and position of maximum thickness at 24% of the chord.

However, these thin airfoils can be problematic. The onset of separation can be dramatic, triggering an equally dramatic sudden stall. It is also hard to make a strong wing this thin. Every time you cut the wing thickness in half, you cut its strength to 25% the original amount.

2.3. XFoil

XFoil[1] is a mature airfoil analysis and design computer program for subsonic flows. It is very well respected in the aerodynamics industry, and best of all it's free. The primary author is Mark Drela, of model glider design fame. It is surprisingly feature rich, but getting accurate results out of it can be a

---

[1]http://raphael.mit.edu/xfoil/

Figure 2.5. Göttingen 397 airfoil
A good airfoil for low Reynolds number applications. Good L/D value.

Figure 2.6. Eppler E71 airfoil
Another good airfoil for low Reynolds number applications. Great for high lift.

frustrating experience. Separation bubbles give it a lot of trouble. Analyses beyond the stall, for very thick airfoils, or for airfoils with sharp angles are bound to be inaccurate.

It is also strictly a subsonic solver, so analyses of airfoils with regions of supersonic flow will not be accurate.

It is a lot easier to predict lift than to predict drag. If the size of a separation bubble is underestimated, both quantities will be affected. When XFoil gets into trouble, it tends to overestimate the lift and underestimate the drag.

2.4. Summary Table

I've included basic physical characteristics and performance data for a few popular airfoils (see Table 2.1 on page 58). The performance data were computed at Reynolds numbers of either 75,000 or 150,000 depending on whether the airfoil is intended for low Reynolds number applications or not.

All of the performance data were calculated using RCadvisor's calculator, which is precomputed using XFoil (see Section 2.3 on page 53). It's an excellent program, but it shouldn't take long to see a couple of places in the table where the results look suspicious.

The camber of the NACA 0018 airfoil is listed as 0.2. Since this is a symmetrical airfoil, the camber should be zero. This is not a large error and is not even XFoil's fault—the problem is entirely within the airfoil coordinates.

Astute readers may notice that the design lift coefficient of the NASA LS(1)-0413 airfoil is listed as 1.04 but I said earlier that this airfoil has a design lift coefficient of 0.4 (hence the name). Yup. This airfoil was designed and tested with full-size airplanes in mind. A Reynolds number of 150,000 is an entirely different ball game.

The two lowest drag airfoils in the table, the Phönix and the SD 7037, both show very high maximum lift to drag ratios. In both of these cases, the peak in efficiency was very sharp, unlikely to be reached in actual use. You want to make sure the airfoil you choose works well at a range of angles of attack and Reynolds numbers. I'll talk more about design robustness later (see Section 8.4.2 on page 162).

Laminar flow airfoils have their point of maximum thickness pushed back in an attempt to delay the onset of turbulent flow (see Figure 2.7 on the next page). In theory these airfoil designs work great. In practice, not so much. The problem is that any slight imperfection in the shape of the wing surface will destroy the effect. In other words, they are not robust in the face of real-life usage. Because of this and their unpredictable stalls, I cannot recommend them.

The moral here is to take a critical eye to any computer simulation results. If it looks too good to be true.... Ultimately it is your responsibility to use, tweak, or just plain outright discard any results obtained.

2.5. Kline-Fogleman

2.5.1. History

In the early 1960s Richard Kline, an advertising agency art director, stumbled upon a new airfoil design concept while folding paper airplanes for his son. He spent four frustrating years trying to get toy companies interested in his design. In 1968 he demonstrated the paper airplane (see Figure 2.8 on the facing page) to photo-retoucher Floyd Fogleman, a pilot and model airplane enthusiast, who declared the design a major breakthrough. The rest, as they say, is history.

Well, not exactly. Despite an incredible amount of buzz surrounding these airfoils in their early years, including feature stories in Time magazine and 60 Minutes, they have never enjoyed much commercial success. In recent years they have become popular with some model airplane designers. Was this a fad or was there really something here? I decided to investigate.

Figure 2.7. North American P-51D Mustang
The first airplane to incorporate a laminar airfoil. Under the rigors of war, the airfoil did not work nearly as well as expected.

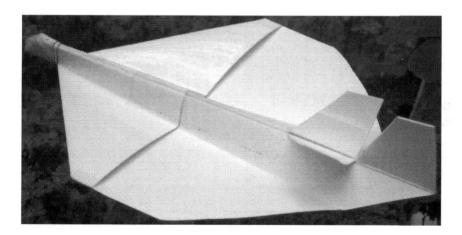

Figure 2.8. Kline-Fogleman paper airplane
Note the step on top of the wing.

Name	Max Camber (%)	Max Thickness (%)	Re (k)	Cl_max	CD_min	L/D_max	Design Cl
AG13	1.9	5.8	75	1.02	0.006	62	0.45
AG25	2.4	7.6	150	1.19	0.008	74	0.69
Clark Y	3.4	11.7	150	1.35	0.009	68	0.64
E71	4.6	5.2	75	1.32	0.016	43	0.68
EMX-07	2.5	9.9	150	1.19	0.010	47	0.72
Göttingen 397	4.0	5.1	75	1.14	0.016	44	0.74
Göttingen 417	6.0	6.0	75	1.40	0.020	58	1.20
MH32	2.4	8.7	150	1.15	0.008	92	0.80
MH45	1.6	9.8	150	1.13	0.010	62	0.84
NACA 0012	0.1	12.0	150	1.06	0.011	39	0.62
NACA 0018	0.2	18.0	150	1.09	0.015	44	1.01
NACA 2412	1.9	12.0	150	1.31	0.011	49	0.88
NASA LS(1)-0413	2.1	13.0	150	1.47	0.016	56	1.04
Phönix	2.8	8.2	150	1.13	0.002	239	0.51
SD 7037	2.9	9.2	150	1.32	0.001	1,220	0.73

Table 2.1. Airfoil properties

2.5.2. Variations

Four variations on the Kline-Fogleman (KFm) airfoil have been published. The original, dubbed KFm1, has a step on the bottom that ends 40% back from the wing's leading edge. This variant has great stall resistance even at very high angles of attack. KFm2 has a step on top that ends at the 50% chord point and produces much more lift than KFm1. Both of these airfoils are good for thicknesses of 7-9% and have good stability. The step height should be 50% of the thickness. The two more advanced variants, KFm3 and KFm4, work better with a thickness of 9-12%. KFm3 has steps on top at the 50% and 75% points. It produces the best lift of all variants. KFm4 is symmetrical with steps on top and bottom at the 50% point and is a great choice for aerobatic airplanes. Each of these steps should be about $\frac{1}{3}$ of the overall thickness (see Figure 2.9 on the next page).

An early misconception that delayed their adoption was the belief that a KFm step had to be used with a flat airfoil (as depicted in Figure 2.9 on the following page). They can be easily added to a traditional airfoil (see Figure 2.10 on page 61).

2.5.3. Published Research

Tests conducted at Notre Dame University by John Nicolaides (an early fan of the airfoil) compared the KFm2 airfoil (step on top) with a flat plate. He measured an increase in lift of 44% and an increase in the L/D ratio of 30%. The problem is, comparing the airfoil against a flat plate is not the most useful comparison. It's like saying that a new design in running shoes is a major breakthrough because a runner wearing them was 44% faster than a barefoot runner. Flat plates are notorious for being poor lift producers.

In 1994 Demeter Fertis reexamined the airfoils. The most promising results were with a NACA 23012 airfoil modified with a KFm2 step that curved up and ended at 75% of the chord. He measured a 50% increase in L/D ratio over the unmodified airfoil at low angles of attack. This airfoil had about the same maximum lift coefficient as the unmodified airfoil, but it did not

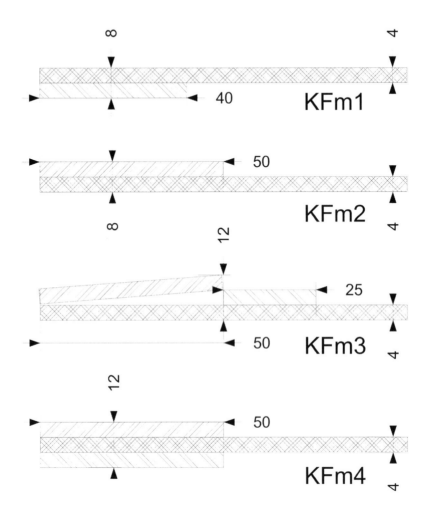

Figure 2.9. KFm airfoils

The dimensions indicate percentage of the wing chord.

Figure 2.10. Clark Y airfoil with KFm1 step

stall until an angle of attack of 38 degrees was reached. There was also about a 50% increase in lift at low angles of attack.

A 1998 study by Finaish and Witherspoon also found some interesting results. They measured modest increases in lift with a NACA 0012 airfoil (see Figure 6.1 on page 116) with a KFm2 step, but at the cost of increased drag. They got excellent results with a KFm1 step, with increased lift and lift/drag ratio over the measured range of 0 to 10 degrees angle of attack.

A recent study by Rich Thompson in 2008 using model airplanes is also very interesting. I have to commend Mr. Thompson on the thoroughness of his research. Every other study that I've mentioned so far was conducted at professional research labs using state-of-the-art wind tunnels. Thompson had no such equipment, so he did his best to objectively gauge the flight characteristics of the various models he built.

I would have preferred it if he had done a double blind study, but otherwise Thompson followed an excellent methodology. He tested several airfoils, including all of the KFm variants. In decreasing order of merit, the airfoils he recommends are as follows:

1. KFm2 (simple top step)

2. KFm3 (compound top step)

3. symmetrical (good for aerobatics)

4. Clark Y (I would use instead a NASA LS(1)-0413)

In 2008 Paul Wheeler experimented by adding a KFm2-like step to the tip of propellers (see Figure 2.11 on the next page). He calls it a Stepped Bevel Airfoil. Wheeler measured a 9% increase in thrust, which I find remarkable. Paul told me that he's using his powered parachute for the testing and plans to continue his research.

A frustrating aspect of these airfoils is that they resist analysis by panel program codes like XFoil. I've tried to analyze them with XFoil myself, but I do not trust the results I got. Some studies have been published in the past (not those mentioned here) that relied on computer analysis exclusively. I find their results highly suspect, too.

2.5.4. Theory

How do these airfoils work? The theory is that a vortex of air forms in the step. It lowers the drag by rotating with the flow of air and discourages separation from occurring. This is a reasonable explanation for how the top surface step works. How a step on the bottom of an airfoil manages to delay separation on the top surface is a neat trick, to say the least. When I asked Richard Kline, the airfoil's inventor, this is what he had to say:

> "To date, there has been no plausible explanation for how the vortex on the bottom works. My guess would be that there is a compression build-up within the vortex that helps produce lift from underneath while exerting a slight forward pressure as well. The pressure within the vortex needs to be equal in both wings at all times. When one wing is tilted upwards, pressure increases on the other wing forcing it to level off. But, this is just a guess on my part."
>
> **Richard Kline**
> *private communication*

Regardless of the actual mechanism, they appear to have some good real world uses.

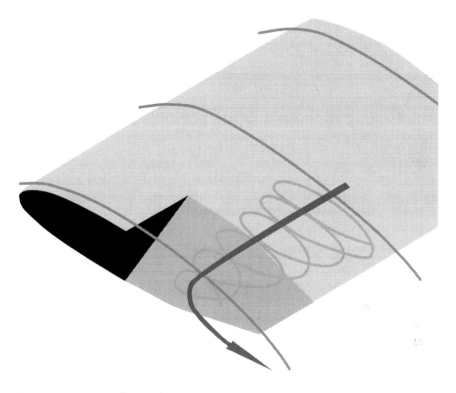

Figure 2.11. Propeller with KFm2 tip
The tip rotates clockwise and up the page. Courtesy of Paul Wheeler.

2.5.5. Applications

These airfoils are a good choice for a model airplane as a step up from a flat plate. A flat plate is likely to be very thin, so it will be weaker or need heavy/expensive reinforcements.

They have also proved their value when a traditional airfoil can be used. Stall resistance is a nice quality to have when the model has to overcome air turbulence. Because of the stall resistance, you will end up with a large speed range, another nice quality. This means that they can be used for lifting heavy loads *and* they can fly fast, too.

It is interesting to note that these modified airfoils had both better lift characteristics and better lift/drag ratios than the original unmodified airfoils. That is very unusual. Since they are so thin, their penetration into wind is very good.

They also have low moment coefficients, allowing a wide center of gravity (CG) range. A normal airfoil is dangerous when the CG is moved back beyond 33% of the airfoil chord. These airfoils are happy with a CG as far back as 40% of the chord. If the CG shifts during flight, you will probably still have good control authority. Because of the stall resistance, control authority is normally excellent. Although not proven by wind tunnel experiments, it appears that these airfoils generate their lift very far back.

The KFm3 airfoil is the best lift producer of the bunch. It is a good choice when the model is heavy. The KFm4 airfoil is an obviously good choice for an aerobatic model. It is the fastest of the four with very fast snap rolls while still providing lots of stability.

Many tests have been conducted with steps having lower depth. As expected, their effects were less pronounced than steps of 50% of the airfoil thickness.

These airfoils are very easy to build. That is a big plus when you are prototyping a new design.

3. Propellers

Calling an airplane propeller a chunk of maple is like calling a violin a wooden box. I suppose it would be technically correct but it would completely fail to grasp the big picture. In fact, for all its apparent simplicity, the propeller is arguably the hardest part of an airplane to understand and the power system component that is easiest to get wrong.

A propeller is like a wing that is turning around in a circle as opposed to moving forward in a straight line. Just like wings, propeller blades are carved in the shape of airfoils (called profiles in Europe). One-third of the pulling power of a propeller is due to the bottom surfaces of the blades pushing back the air. Two-thirds is due to the partial vacuum as a result of lift produced from the top surface. This lift acts as a thrust amplifier and is key to propeller efficiency.

3.1. History

We owe the beginning of modern propeller theory to the Wright brothers. Wilbur Wright was the first to realize that a propeller behaves like a rotating wing. The efficiency of his propeller was 70%, which is excellent, when the best anybody else had been able to achieve was 50%. A modern propeller will be lucky to get above 80%.

3.2. Background

Half of the area swept by the propeller blades lies within a radius of 71%. Closer to the propeller hub, the thrust produced is low because the angular velocity is low.

Closer to the tip the rotational velocity is high, but then tip losses come into effect (just like a wing). But there are other reasons why the propeller blade tips produce less thrust than might be expected. The blade chord is usually smaller towards the tips because of structural concerns. There's just too much momentum and bending loads out towards the tips.

The angle of attack of the blade tip is usually less than expected as a compromise to give the propeller good efficiency over a wider range of speeds. The tips are also often made thinner and at a lower angle of attack to counteract Mach effects (more on this soon).

A common technique for analyzing propellers involves using the so-called representative blade element theory. This theory assumes that the entire propeller consists of a thin airfoil at a radius of 75%. The theory works surprisingly well, once the appropriate constants are plugged into the formulas.

3.3. Diameter and Pitch

Propellers are designated by two numbers, the diameter and the pitch. It is common to see a designation such as 12x6, meaning a diameter of 12 inches and a pitch of 6 inches. Outside the U.S. the numbers might designate millimeters, though using inches is common.

The diameter is easy enough to understand. It is the distance from tip to tip on a two-bladed propeller. Pitch, however, is a lot harder to grasp and the name doesn't help much. The meaning is quite similar to the pitch of a common screw (in fact, propellers were originally called airscrews for that reason). Imagine the propeller moving through a solid, such as a block of softened butter. Pitch is the distance that the propeller would move forward when turned one revolution. A much easier to understand unit would have been blade angle, so that a 12x6 propeller would be a 12x9°. Oh well.

There are a couple of quirks related to measuring propeller pitch that I need to mention. First, it is measured at the 75% radius point. This should make sense after reading the previous section. Second, the angle of the blade is measured relative to the bottom of the blade airfoil. It'll be closer to the zero lift angle (the angle of attack when the airfoil produces no lift) than to the chord line, used to measure the angle of attack of wings.

The thrust produced by a propeller varies in proportion to the RPM squared and the diameter raised to the fourth power. This means that a propeller spinning at 10,000 RPM will produce twice as much thrust when spun at 14,000 RPM. A 12 inch diameter propeller produces double the thrust of a 10 incher. In fact, if you double the diameter of the propeller, you'll be producing 16 times the thrust of the original propeller.

3.4. Problems Analyzing

Propellers are the most problematic power system components to analyze. I find this very ironic, since physically they are the simplest.

There are several reasons for this. It is not uncommon for the propeller diameter or pitch to be mislabelled. Maybe a 30 cm propeller is being sold as a 12 inch propeller. A 0.12 inch difference in diameter can make a big difference in performance! Independent testing has shown that significant errors in printed pitch values are present in some model airplane propellers. I'm certain that inconsistent measurement techniques is a major source of these errors. Manufacturing variations due to the molding techniques used are also a potential culprit.

It gets worse. A propeller blade changes angle of attack and airfoil section throughout its entire length. Different materials respond differently to the loads imposed on them. Molded propellers are very susceptible to variations between samples. A given manufacturer may sell six different 12x6 propellers, all in different product lines with very different performance characteristics.

The efficiency of a system is the ratio of the useful work produced to the amount of energy used to produce it. The input energy to a propeller is the rotational velocity and shaft torque. The output is thrust. To measure the efficiency of a propeller we need to know the RPM, how much energy is needed to turn it at that RPM, and how much thrust is being produced.

There are two propeller constants that are used to characterize the performance of a given propeller. The first is n100W, which is the RPM of the propeller when it is absorbing 100 watts of power. The other is n10N, which is the RPM of the propeller when it is producing 10 newtons of thrust. Both of these are defined to be measured at zero airspeed and in a standard atmosphere.

If the data were measured at a non-zero airspeed, we also need to know the airspeed value, since that augments the thrust being produced. The faster you are going, the harder it is to produce a given amount of thrust, so we need to take the airspeed into account.

Unfortunately, I'm not aware of a single propeller manufacturer that provides power required and thrust available data for their propellers. Aero--naut has charts of power required at a given RPM for their propellers. A couple of other manufacturers provide thrust data for some of their propellers. And that's about it, folks!

Using a thrust stand, a wattmeter, and a tachometer to take propeller measurements at home is not too hard to do. If the propeller is not stalled and you follow a good procedure, you can get excellent test data. I just really wish that manufacturers would rise to the challenge and provide these data for us.

3.5. Spinners

The roots of the propeller blades must be quite strong to keep the blades from flying off. They are also useless aerodynamically. The central 25% of the diameter of a propeller could only generate about 2% of the thrust even if it had a nice airfoil shape to it.

Most model airplane propellers are flown without a spinner, which is a mistake. The spinner is there for more than just looks. It helps to push the air out towards the part of the propeller that can efficiently generate lift. To be most effective, the spinner should be about 25% of the diameter. On a 12 inch propeller, that makes the spinner 3 inches wide. This is huge. I've never seen anybody use a spinner that large, unless it's an unusual scale job.

3.6. Mach Effects

The Mach number is the speed of an object relative to the speed of sound, which is about 750 mi/h (1200 km/h). Mach 0.5 is therefore half the speed of sound or about 375 mi/h (600 km/h). When an airfoil approaches the speed of sound, it experiences dramatic increases in both lift and drag. It is this increase in drag that led to the term "the sound barrier".

The air speeds up as it travels over the top surface of an airfoil. The *critical Mach number* is the airspeed of an airfoil where any part of the airfoil reaches Mach 1. Due to the local increase in airspeed over an airfoil, the critical Mach number for an airfoil can be as low as Mach 0.5.

It's not too hard for the tip of a propeller, even on a model airplane, to reach speeds where Mach effects come into play. The 12x6 propeller mentioned above might surpass its critical Mach number when just one horsepower (745 watts) of power is applied to it and it reaches an RPM of 10,500. If any more power than that is applied, you'll be in an uphill battle.

It's actually worse than that. The tip speed is a combination of rotational velocity and forward air speed. At a flying speed of 50 mi/h (80 km/h), the critical RPM will be about 1% lower in this example.

There is one big caveat in all of this. The tips on most propellers are fairly thin. This is usually done for structural reasons, but it also delays the onset of Mach effects. A properly designed wood propeller has a critical Mach number of around 0.8, a carbon fiber propeller's is 0.9. Most likely, your propeller will be somewhere in between the two extremes (0.5 to 0.9).

There are three ways to delay the onset of Mach effects on an airfoil: make it thin (<10%), take out the camber, and use a supercritical airfoil. Making the airfoil thinner is easy but it will make it weaker. A supercritical airfoil has a relatively flat top in order to avoid a sharp rise in the local airspeed. In practice, all these techniques are used together.

3.7. Efficiency

The three most important characteristics of a propeller from an efficiency standpoint are diameter, diameter, and diameter. The larger, the better. In fact, the primary reason why a three-bladed propeller is less efficient than an equivalent two-bladed propeller is not because of interference between the blades (as it is commonly believed), but because of the need to reduce the diameter.

Increasing the propeller diameter won't improve the efficiency if the airpeed and RPM stay the same. The gain in efficiency comes from the reduced RPM and greater volume of air that is accelerated less than before. Since the power coming from the motor/engine is close to constant, the RPM will drop automatically.

Increasing the diameter won't increase the propeller's Reynolds number if you lower the RPM to compensate. A propeller blade normally operates at a Reynolds number of 100,000 to 400,000, so chances are that you are not suffering too much from Reynolds effects.

The efficiency of a propeller goes down as the airspeed increases, the only exception being when the propeller is stalled right at the start of the take-off run. The angle of attack of the propeller blades also goes down as the airspeed increases.

Here's a tip. If the propeller starts making a lot of noise, throttle back. Normally the noise from a propeller increases linearly as the RPM increases. Unusually high noise from a propeller indicates turbulence close to Mach 1 and reduced efficiency. Avoid it.

3.8. Zero Airspeed

If the blade angle is too high, the propeller could be starting the take-off run in a stalled state. For a thin airfoil this could be as low as 10 degrees (the way propeller blade angle is measured). This is not quite as bad as most people imagine.

A stalled airfoil still produces lift, despite what you may think you know. It's just that it produces less lift than the maximum **and** it also produces a lot of drag. In a flying airplane the drag slows it down, so it produces even less lift and it falls out of the sky. But extra drag on a spinning propeller blade just slows it down. It is still producing plenty of lift, so there is no danger of not having enough thrust to get the airplane moving forward.

In case you are wondering, this is the source of the sudden unloading that some propellers experience as the airplane starts accelerating. It is much more noticeable with high pitched propellers, since they are likely to be more stalled to begin with.

By definition, the efficiency of a propeller is zero when the forward speed is zero. It's a little hard to understand why it has to be this way. Let me try and explain.

Imagine a 1,000 pound cement block that is bolted down to the floor. You push and push on it with all your force. If you're built anything like me, the block will not budge. Despite all the energy you've expended in trying to move it, you have nothing to show for your efforts. You've accomplished no useful work.

A propeller works the same way. It can turn as fast as it wants and cause a great deal of air to move, but if there is no forward movement, there is no useful work accomplished. The goal of an airplane propeller is to pull the airplane forward, not to cause a pleasant breeze or a lot of noise.

The efficiency of a system is measured by its ability to convert energy into useful work. That is the textbook definition, and is the key to understanding the propeller efficiency formula. Since without forward motion there is no useful work being accomplished, by definition, the efficiency of the propeller has to be zero. In turn, since the overall power system efficiency is the product of the efficiency of every power-related component, it too has to be equal to zero.

3.9. Advance Ratio

A useful value to compute for a spinning propeller is the advance ratio (3.1).

$$AdvanceRatio = \frac{airplaneAirspeed}{\frac{revolutions}{second} * propellerDiameter} \quad (3.1)$$

The angle of attack of the blades of two propellers (measured at the same point in the radius) will be the same if their advance ratio is the same.

More importantly, the efficiency of a propeller will always be the same at the same advance ratio. That means that if a given propeller is 75% efficient at a flying speed of 25 mi/h and 12,000 RPM, then it will be 75% efficient at an airspeed of 50 mi/h and 6,000 RPM. The only caveat is that sometimes Reynolds and Mach effects can throw a monkey wrench into the numbers. But under most circumstances the relation holds true.

Thin blades on propellers are generally more efficient, but that also narrows the range of advance ratio values where the propeller has high efficiency. So if your propeller is very thin, be extra careful.

The combination of rotational velocity and forward airspeed results in the angle that the propeller blade is moving forward through the air. Propeller theory states that the propeller efficiency will be highest when this angle is 45 degrees. That means that for every inch that the 75% radius of the propeller rotates, it moves forward one inch. Most model airplane propellers rotate too fast and move forward too slowly. The good news here is that the efficiency will be reasonable as long as the angle is between 30 and 60 degrees.

4. Structures

4.1. Materials

4.1.1. Material Properties

It can be instructive to look at the properties of some materials commonly used in model airplane structures (see Table 4.2 on page 79). Note that there are no absolute values in the table. All of the values have been scaled, with the tensile and compressive values sharing a common scale. The main values compared are for weight, yield tensile strength, yield compressive strength, and modulus of elasticity.

Tensile strength is the stress at which a material breaks or permanently deforms when pulled. Compressive strength is similar but when the material is being pushed. The yield point is when the material deforms permanently (as opposed to springing back). Modulus of elasticity is how stiff a material is. The higher the value, the stiffer.

Wood is rarely tested for tensile strength parallel to the grain (where it is strongest), so the modulus of rupture was substituted as a conservative estimate. Aramid, fiberglass and graphite are assumed to be embedded in an epoxy resin matrix.

Most materials that we are interested in are stronger in tension than in compression. Some call this the wet noodle theory. Like a wet noodle, they collapse easily if you push against it, but are stronger when you pull. Steel and iron are notable exceptions. Aramid (Kevlar) is unusually weak in compression. This is because it has trouble bonding with epoxy.

There are some interesting observations that can be made. As expected, the foams are uniformly weak (labelled EPP, EPS and XPS in the table). Note how all the woods are clustered together in the middle of the table. They are more similar to each other than different from each other. Strength in tension is pretty good for all the woods. Carbon fiber (graphite) is unusual in that it is very strong and good at both tension and compression. Too bad it's relatively heavy and very expensive. Looking at stiffness by weight, the foams, graphite and aramid are the only standouts.

4.1.2. Polystyrene Foam (EPS and XPS)

Polystyrene is a polymer manufactured from petroleum. It is a very commonly used plastic. Look for it in products such as disposable cutlery and disposable drinking cups.

When expanded (EPS) and shaped into white drinking cups, it is known by the common name styrofoam. The problem is, Styrofoam is a brand name that belongs to Dow Chemical. Dow has never manufactured foam drinking cups and they have never licensed the name to be used for drinking cups. Oops. Expanded polystyrene is low in weight and low in strength. It is rarely the best choice as a building material.

Extruded polystyrene foam (XPS) is a nice material. This is the stuff that Dow calls Styrofoam and is colored blue as a trademark. Owens Corning sells a similar material with embedded fiberglass fibers and is colored pink. The problem with the pink foam is that is is designed to snap when bent. Blue foam is much more likely to bend and bounce back. Unless you plan to never crash, avoid the pink stuff. This is the same stuff that Midwest sells under the brand name Cellfoam 88. It is also the material found between two sheets of paper in foamboard. A brand name for foamboard is foamcore. Finally, it's what Depron is made from. Given that this is a manufactured product, it can be made in a range of densities. But for the purpose of model building they are all very similar.

4.1.3. Polypropylene Foam (EPP)

Polypropylene (polypro or PP) is another polymer. It is made from propy-
lene, a gas extracted from petroleum or natural gas deposits. It is commonly
used to make ropes that float and are water resistant. It has excellent fatigue
resistance, making it useful for making hinges (the lids of Tic Tac containers
are made out of this). Rubbermaid and Sterilite make a large range of trash
cans and other plastic containers out of the stuff. 3M Scotch Strapping tape
(both the backing and the filaments) is made out of this. It is highly resistant
to chemical solvents. Epoxy does not stick to it.

   Expanded polypropylene (EPP) is a foam that is also used to build model
aircraft. It is very lightweight. It has low stiffness, but that is what gives it
excellent impact resistance. Pool noodles are made out of EPP.

4.1.4. Wood

Don't make the mistake of dismissing wood as old fashioned. It's inexpensive, easily shaped, readily available, and quite strong.

   Balsa and spruce are much more expensive than pine, birch, Douglas-fir
(which is not part of the fir family, but that is another story) or bamboo.
Buying balsa can be justified when you need the light weight. It's harder
to justify buying spruce, except of course when it's easier to find in the size
that you need.

   As can be seen from the table, there is nothing magical about spruce. It
is just another wood. It was selected a hundred years ago by the aircraft
industry as the wood of choice more than anything because it was plentiful
and therefore easily available in high quality. Neither of those qualities are
any longer true.

   As a rule, wood is about twice as strong in tension as in compression. It
has decent stiffness.

   The strength of wood increases as it gets drier. Like a piece of paper, it
loses much of its strength as it gets wetter. It's an old trick to soak a piece of
wood before bending it easily around a curve.

A common fallacy is that wood is somehow stabilized once it has been dried. *That is not true.* Unprotected wood is continually exchanging moisture with the surrounding air (see Table 4.1 on the facing page).

Air-dried lumber for construction has a moisture content of about 15%. Furniture-grade wood is oven (kiln) dried to about half of that. Wood can rot once it reaches a moisture content of 20% or higher. Surprisingly, wood held underwater does not rot because the fungi that makes it decay needs lots of oxygen. This does not mean that there aren't other organisms that might attack the wood while underwater.

Almost all problems with using wood have moisture as their root cause. Wood moisture meters are relatively inexpensive, but some common sense is all you need to stay out of trouble. Bottom line, seal the wood and it will last much longer.

A column made out of wood with a length to width ratio greater than 11 is subject to buckling. For example, suppose you make a pushrod out of $\frac{1}{4}$ inch balsa. This means that at lengths of three inches or more, you won't get the full strength of the wood unless the pushrod is supported somehow. Since the buckling strength of a column decreases as the square of its length, very quickly your pushrod won't be any good for pushing (it'll still be fine for pulling, though). I'm not saying that you couldn't build a pushrod out of balsa, since that is clearly done regularly. What I'm saying is that it will have to be a lot thicker than dictated by the compressive strength requirements alone. The buckling strength of a column is proportional to the modulus of elasticity of the material. A column made out of carbon fiber will be about 13 times more resistant to buckling than one made out of wood.

4.1.5. Fiberglass

Fiberglass is literally made from glass drawn into long filaments. It has excellent strength in tension and stiffness, though aramid is much better (and costlier).

Rel humidity (%)	Resulting wood moisture content (%)
0	0
25	5
50	9
65	12
75	14
100	30

Table 4.1. Change in wood moisture
Unless sealed, wood is constantly changing its moisture content.

4.1.6. Aramid

Aramid is a very strong and heat-resistant synthetic fiber. It was first introduced by DuPont under the name Nomex. It is also known as Kevlar and Twaron.

These fibers are very abrasion resistant, do not absorb moisture, have very little stretch, are very stiff, and are very strong in tension (not so much in compression).

Different in chemical structure but similar in physical properties, high-performance polyethylene is known as Spectra or Dyneema. Spectra fishing line is easy to find and relatively inexpensive.

Aramid and Spectra work great for pull-pull servo connections and for overall strengthening. Pull-pull control surface connections use two lines of aramid or Spectra (it needs to be strong and not stretch) between the servo and the control surface. One line is attached to each side of the servo horn and control surface. This is a lighter weight alternative to the traditional single stiff rod that is used for both pushing and pulling. When you only have to worry about tension, you can usually use less material.

4.1.7. Carbon Fiber

The king of fibers. First made by heating rayon until it carbonized. It is about 94% pure carbon (graphite) atoms aligned in a crystalline structure. It has outstanding compressive strength and stiffness. The tensile strength is not bad, but aramid and fiberglass are better.

Carbon atoms are found in nature in mostly two forms: graphite and diamonds. Pencil lead is almost entirely made out of graphite. Carbon fiber has its carbon atoms aligned into extremely thin fibers. Like the alignment of carbon atoms in a diamond, it is this regular pattern that gives carbon fiber its extreme strength.

Due to its extreme stiffness, carbon fiber catches many of its users by surprise when it just snaps without warning. From a structural design point of view, metals have one advantage here. They bend and deform long before they break, giving ample warning that something is wrong.

Diamonds, even though they are electrical insulators, have the best thermal conductivity of any material. Graphite is a very good electrical conductor. This is of concern with the new Spread Spectrum (2.4GHz) radio systems, since carbon fiber in the model will block these signals.

Hollow carbon fiber tubes are either plain pultruded or wrapped. Both are incredibly strong, but the wrapped tubes are also incredibly stiff. Both types are commonly used as arrow shafts and in the frameworks of kites. As with all high quality carbon fiber products, the sky is pretty much the only limit as far as price. I've found good deals in broken arrow shafts at the local archery range and on-line in kite tubes with blemishes. Look around—it's worth it!

4.1.8. Metals

Metals such as aluminum and steel have good strength and stiffness, though they are better in compression than in tension. They are relatively heavy and difficult to shape by the average modeler.

	Wgt	Tensile str	/wgt	Compr str	/wgt	Mod elast	/wgt
EPP	1	2.6	2.7	1.6	1.7	1	1.0
EPS	1	1.2	1.2	1.0	1.0	294	283.4
XPS	2	5	2.9	2.7	1.5	342	189.0
Balsa	8	209	28.3	144	19.5	334	43.4
W pine	18	647	36.8	336	19.1	988	54.1
S spruce	19	680	36.8	374	20.2	1,062	55.3
Y poplar	20	673	34.7	369	19.0	1,069	53.0
D-fir	23	827	37.2	482	17.6	1,319	57.2
Ramin	25	1,233	51.3	672	27.9	1,468	58.8
Y birch	30	1,107	38.6	545	19.0	1,360	45.7
Red oak	30	953	32.7	451	15.5	1,232	40.7
Bamboo	39	1,586	41.8	667	17.6	1,335	33.9
Aramid	66	13,333	208.3	2,667	41.7	12,857	193.4
C fiber	74	12,000	167.4	12,000	167.4	16,240	218.2
S fibergls	125	14,600	121.7	4,927	41.1	7,815	62.7
Aluminum	133	3,000	23.4	2,467	19.3	7,240	54.5
Steel	374	14,667	40.8	16,000	44.5	20,300	54.3

Table 4.2. Material property ratios

4.2. Adhesives

Modern adhesives (glues) are all synthetic compounds that are formulated in an infinite variety for specific uses. The characteristics described here apply to those formulations commonly available in the market.

Trying to mention all glues commonly used would be futile. Here are the ones I consider the most important.

4.2.1. Cyanoacrylates

Also known as Krazy Glue or CAs. CA glues polymerize and harden in the presence of water or moisture. They dry very quickly and are very strong. Bonds reach their full strength in about two hours. Since so little of the glue is used at a time, the joints are lightweight. Baking soda can be used as a gap-filling agent. A small amount of water can be sprayed onto a joint to speed up the drying process (CA is waterproof).

They bond extremely well to many materials, including metals. Adhesion to glass is normally poor.

If you are not going to be using an open container for a while, store it in the freezer. Wrap large bottles in black electrical tape to delay its deterioration from UV light. Use acetone (nail polish remover) to soften cured CA. Storing the part to be separated in a freezer will make the glued joint brittle.

Do you hate clogged tips? To eliminate them, squeeze the bottle slightly *before* you tip the bottle over. Then when you are done using it, release the pressure before you put the cap back on. The excess CA inside the tip will get sucked back down into the container. Voilá!

CAs react violently with cotton and wool. Do not wear cotton gloves while working with CA! They also bond extremely well to skin. Keep a bottle of nail polish remover handy, just in case.

Their primary disadvantages are their high cost and the fact that they dry rock hard and are therefore difficult to sand. They do not work well if the part needs flexibility in the joint. Also, the shearing (twisting) strength of the joints is low.

The drying process releases heat, so CA normally cannot be used with heat sensitive materials like foams. A different formulation dubbed "foam-safe CA" avoids this problem and also releases fewer fumes which some are sensitive to.

Because of their high cost and brittleness, I rarely use CAs anymore. Their primary value is probably to facilitate quick field repairs.

4.2.2. Polyurethanes

Originally introduced into the United States as Gorilla and Excel glues. Also known as Sumo glue. PUR glues were first used in 1985 as a glue for binding books. It is widely used today in woodworking. Similar to CA glues, it is waterproof and moisture triggers the drying process. Unlike CA, though, it can be sanded easily after it dries. There will be some flexibility in the joints, and the cost is a little high but not as much as CAs. The parts can be handled after half an hour and it'll be fully cured after two days.

Dogs like to eat this glue. Even a small amount will expand and block their digestive system. Don't kill the pooch.

I have found that these glues work extremely well with foams. The joints are incredibly strong. It is clear that a chemical reaction has taken place. Separating two pieces of foam joined with this glue results in a good-sized chunk of foam staying attached to the glue. It is also not too heavy, a disadvantage of epoxies.

What's not to like? Well, a lot of people don't like using this glue because it expands slowly during the first hour as it dries. You have several options for dealing with this. You can ignore it and just use a sharp blade to cut-off the excess after it dries. Wiping away the excess as it dries is another option. I personally always forget about the drying glue and never wipe it down in time. A better solution is to use masking tape to control where the glue expands into. The tape peels off easily after the glue dries, and you will end up with a beautiful filleted joint.

Wearing gloves is recommended not because of a toxicity problem but because the glue is hard to remove from the hands. Acetone, mineral spirits or denatured alcohol can be used for cleanup while the glue is still wet.

The more moisture in the joint, the faster the glue will dry. Non-porous surfaces will take a lot longer. I sometimes wet down with water the parts that I'm about to glue. Another technique used by some is to drop globs of the glue into a container full of water. Let them soak in the water for a few minutes, and then scoop up a glob and put it on the joint. The glue will be pre-expanded and it will dry very quickly.

4.2.3. Epoxies

The epoxy adhesive industry is huge. It is the adhesive of choice to use with fiberglass, carbon fiber and other composite materials. It works wonderfully with wood, foam, metal, glass, and many other materials. Extremely strong, they are very resistant to heat (when heat cured) and chemicals. Formulations can be very fast or slow setting.

A couple of problems with epoxies keep it from being more widely used. One is that it requires the thorough mixing of two parts together. You are guaranteed to either mix too much or too little. Too little can be disastrous. It is also fairly heavy. I have several friends that have developed allergies to uncured epoxy resins. You don't want to have this. Of all the adhesives in common use, epoxy is the most toxic because of this.

4.3. Wing Structures

The primary load on a wing is the bending force that pushes it upwards. This bending moment is overwhelmingly concentrated at the wing root. One quarter of the way out from the wing root, this force has already dropped to half its original value (see Table 4.3 on the next page).

Normally our focus is on making a strong wing, but making a stiff wing is usually harder to achieve. In other words, once you've made it stiff enough,

Station (%)	Bending moment (%)	Shear load (%)
Root	100	100
12	75	88
25	50	75
50	21	50
75	4	25
Tip	0	0

Table 4.3. Wing loads

it'll also probably be strong enough. I always keep a close eye on the moment of elasticity of the materials I use.

The specific loads on a wing in flight are as follows. The upper spar is in compression. The lower spar is in tension. The forces are pushing the upper spar down and pushing the lower spar up. The shear or spar web's main job is to keep the two spars apart. There will also be significant shear forces running along the middle of the shear web, right in between the two spars. This shear force decreases linearly along the span (see Table 4.3).

4.3.1. Bending Moment

There is an easy formula for estimating the bending moment on the wing spar (4.1).

$$BendingMoment = (\frac{wingSpan}{4}) * maximumLoad \qquad (4.1)$$

We need to estimate the maximum load that the wings are required to support. We can either base it on the maximum flight load or the maximum launch load. In circling thermal flight, it normally doesn't make sense to circle at a bank angle greater than 45 degrees. That imposes a load on the wings 1.41 times greater than the level flight load. It is customary to use a

50% safely factor for flight loads, so that makes it 2.12. For the launch load, we could use half the breaking load of the winch line.

Since the weight of a wing is normally distributed along its entire span, it does not impose a load at the root. You should subtract the weight of the wing from the level flight load (in other words, the model's flying weight).

Note that in a full-size normal category airplane, the maximum expected flight load is 3.8 times the entire weight and the safety factor adds 50% to make the design load limit 570% the airplane's weight. For an aerobatic full-size airplane, the maximum expected flight load is 6 times its flying weight. Model airplanes normally use design load limits between 5 and 10.

For example, assume we have a two meter glider with a two pound (0.91 kg) weight without the wing. We will base our estimate on the flight load. Using our equation, we get 83 in*lb (0.96 m*kg). That is the bending moment at the wing root. Use Table 4.3 on the preceding page to compute the bending moment along the wingspan. What can you do with this information? Well, doing a full spar strength analysis is probably more trouble than it's worth. But knowing this value can be very useful in comparing the strength needed by different designs.

4.3.2. Main Spar

Putting a spar joiner right at the wing root always struck me as a poor design decision. Why put a heavy joint right at the point of the wing that needs to be strongest? There are other alternatives to adding dihedral to a wing, such as using sweep. If the sweep is not too much, you can still use a straight spar. Another option is a cranked wing (see Figure 4.1 on the next page).

Since most materials are stronger in tension than in compression, you should make the upper spar about 50% thicker than the lower spar. Don't put lightening holes in the spar web. They'd significantly decrease its ability to withstand the shear forces from the wing bending, for almost no savings in weight.

Figure 4.1. Jodel Dauphin
A cranked wing design that avoids having a heavy spar joiner at the wing root. The center section of the wing is built in one piece. All the dihedral is in the outer wing panels.

An excellent design is the box spar, with upper and lower spars and vertical-grained shear webs at the front and back sides. Taper the width of each spar out to the tip to 25% of the width at the root.

Wings with two spar boxes have better strength to weight ratios than wings with just one main spar box. Put the front spar box at the maximum thickness point of the airfoil or at about 20% back from the leading edge of the wing. Put the rear spar box at about 60% back. Make the rear spar box half the strength of the one in front.

A common technique is to use a round solid rod as a spar. A better solution is to use a solid vertical rectangular spar (also called a blade spar). In fact, for the same weight and height, the blade spar will be 31% stronger than a solid round rod. You should be able to make the blade taller, in which case it will be much stronger for the same weight.

5. Wings

5.1. Aspect Ratio

The induced drag of a wing is inversely proportional to the aspect ratio (5.1). The aspect ratio is a comparison of the length of a wing to the overall wing size. A high aspect ratio is used by gliders with their skinny wings. A low aspect ratio is used in delta winged jets (see Figure 5.9 on page 102).

Double the aspect ratio, and you cut in half the induced drag for a given amount of lift. If a low sink rate or high climb rate is important, you want a high aspect ratio wing.

$$AspectRatio = \frac{wingSpan^2}{wingArea} \qquad (5.1)$$

The main problem with high aspect ratio wings is making them strong enough. High performance sailplanes (both models and full-size) rely almost exclusively on fancy composites to make those long skinny wings strong enough.

Since high aspect ratio wings are more efficient at producing lift, their lift generation ability is more sensitive to angle of attack changes. Bottom line is that they are more affected by wind gusts. For flying in windy conditions, use low aspect ratio wings.

Below an aspect ratio of 4 the efficiency of a wing drops dramatically. If you have control over this, keep the aspect ratio between 5 and 7.

If the wing aspect ratio is less than 3 or so, then the choice of airfoil won't make much of a difference. The wing will start behaving like a flat plate and won't generate much lift, either.

I was fortunate to attend the Keystone Radio Control (KRC) Club Fun Fly in 1998. This was the biggest electric model airplane meet in the world at the time. As it turned out, this was the last year that it was held. Everybody that was anybody in the sport was there. After watching some model jets with very low aspect ratio wings and flat airfoils, I turned to my friend Dereck who had come up from Maryland with me. I shared my surprise at seeing the great performance from the model jets. Before Dereck got a chance to respond, a voice over my right shoulder exclaimed "with very low aspect ratios, the airfoil doesn't matter." I turned towards the voice, and it was Keith Shaw. After watching his amazing flight demo earlier that day, I was completely speechless.

5.1.1. Inverse Zimmerman

With very low aspect ratios of two or less, your span efficiency is going to be terrible. One way to combat this is by putting the maximum span location as far back as possible on the wing. You get this with a plain rectangular planform, but the separation drag at the tips will be bad. A better choice is the so-called Inverse Zimmerman (see Figure 5.1 on page 90) wing planform.

This planform puts the maximum span location 75% of the way back on the wing. C. H. Zimmerman invented this planform shape in 1935. But he had the bulge facing forward, at 25% of the chord. Wing tunnel testing has determined that it works much better when placed near the rear, hence the "inverse Zimmerman" name.

Here are parametric equations in case you want to draw your own. Don't let the math scare you. A Zimmerman planform is just a distorted ellipse.

$$f_x(t) = \frac{wingSpan}{2}\cos(t) \tag{5.2}$$

$$f_y(t) = \frac{chord}{4}(2\sin(t) + abs(\sin(t)) - 1) \tag{5.3}$$

$$wingSpan = \frac{\pi * aspectRatio * chord}{4} \tag{5.4}$$

$$t = 0 \ldots 2\pi \tag{5.5}$$

These wing planforms are both beautiful and efficient. I'm including out-lines for aspect ratios of 0.5 to 2.0 to make them easier to use (see Figure 5.1 on the next page). The front view incorporates a gently sloping shape to add some dihedral (see equations below). I'm including outlines for 3%, 4.5% and 6% wing thicknesses (see Figure 5.2 on page 91).

$$f_x(t) = \frac{wingSpan}{2}\cos(t) \tag{5.6}$$

$$f_y(t) = \min(2 * \sin(t) * wingThickness, 0) \tag{5.7}$$

$$t = 0 \ldots 2\pi \tag{5.8}$$

Airfoil theory says that these very low aspect ratios behave like flat plates as far as lift generation. But putting a real airfoil shape on a Zimmerman planform won't hurt. Since it's a plank tailless, you'll need a thin airfoil with a positive moment coefficient (see Section 5.8.5 on page 113).

If the aspect ratio is greater than two, minimizing the induced drag is still important, but now you need to be a little more concerned about separation drag. A Zimmerman planform would be expensive to build and unneces-sary. Stick a Hörner wing tip on a conventional rectangular or trapezoidal planform and leave it at that.

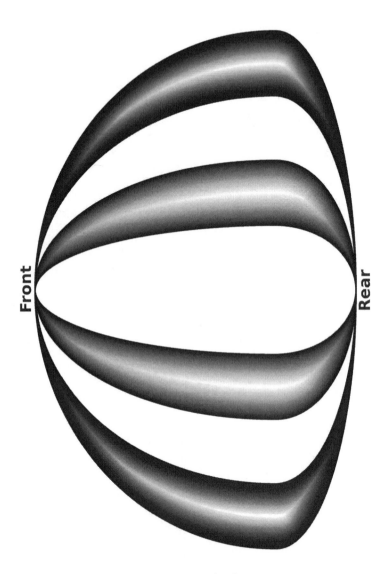

Figure 5.1. Inv Zimmerman wing planform
Includes outlines for aspect ratios 0.5, 1.0, 1.5 and 2.0.

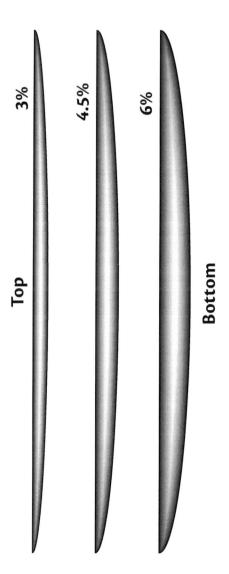

Figure 5.2. Zimmerman dihedral
3%, 4.5% and 6% wing thicknesses.

5.2. Wing area

Wing area determines the airplane's wing loading. The airplane's wing loading requirements are normally dictated by the takeoff distance and climb rate goals. On the other hand, a high wing loading results in a faster cruise speed and better gust resistance. Flaps can be used to widen the performance envelope of the airplane.

5.3. Taper Ratio

The most aerodynamically efficient shape for a wing is elliptical, regardless of the aspect ratio. It produces the minimum amount of induced drag for a given wingspan in the process of generating lift. Very few full-size airplanes have been built with elliptical planforms, since they are costly to build and the actual gain in efficiency over a tapered rectangular wing for typical aspect ratios is very small. Elliptical wings also tend to stall all at once, which is not a desirable characteristic.

The most famous full-size airplane with an elliptical planform is the Supermarine Spitfire (see Figure 5.3 on the facing page), a British World War II fighter. A requirement from the government was the ability to internally mount four machine guns in each wing. The only way to do this was by having a relatively wide chord out to the wing tips, so an elliptical planform was chosen. Having a larger wing area permitted the use of a thinner airfoil which in turn gave it an excellent maximum airspeed. When flying at 350 mi/h (550 km/h), a Spitfire only requires 800 pounds (350 kg) of thrust.

A rectangular wing has about 7% lower efficiency than the 2D airfoils used. A tapered wing with a tip chord 45% of the size of the root chord is about 1% less efficient than the elliptical ideal. This taper ratio is the closest approximation to an elliptical planform, but the entire wing will also tend to stall at the same time.

The elliptical shape is optimal only if the weight of the wing structure is ignored. Because the bending load penalty is so high, more tapered wings are also more structurally efficient. For example, a taper ratio of 0.1 yields a

Figure 5.3. Supermarine Spitfire
Beautiful elliptical wing planform. The location of the four internal machine
guns have been marked with X characters.

drag reduction of 12% over an elliptical planform. This wing would have a longer wingspan but the same wing area and weight.

Rectangular wings have high inertia that lowers their roll rates. They are also structurally inefficient. Small tips are less aerodynamically efficient due to lower Reynolds numbers and are prone to tip stalling. A good compromise is a tip chord of 60% of the size of the root, since the loss of aerodynamic efficiency is only about 4%, it won't tip stall, and it is also reasonably structurally efficient.

For a quick approximation of where the stall will start on a wing, use (5.9). The value is the distance from the centerline as a fraction of half the wingspan. Note that wing sweep pushes the stall location outwards.

$$StallStart_{pos} \approx 1 - taperRatio \qquad (5.9)$$

5.4. Sweep

There are some good reasons for sweeping back the wing of a model airplane. Sweeping a wing increases its apparent chord size, which is good for increasing the Reynolds number. 10 degrees of sweep (measured at the 25% chord line) is roughly equivalent to one degree of dihedral.

Sweeping a wing decreases the maximum amount of lift it can generate (see Table 5.1 on the facing page). It also lowers the effective aspect ratio. Generally speaking, avoid having more than 20 degrees of sweep. Sometimes having a lot of sweep is the best compromise. This is often true in tailless designs.

5.4.1. Wing Fences

As the sweep angle of a wing is increased, the likelihood of tip stalls increases as well. Crossflow can also lead to turbulence in the center section of tailless designs. Both of these undesirable effects can be remedied by the use of wing fences.

Sweep (°)	CL_{max} loss (%)
0	0.0
5	0.4
10	1.5
15	3.4
20	6.0
25	9.4
30	13.4
35	18.1
40	23.4
45	29.3

Table 5.1. CL_{max} loss due to wing sweep

Wing fences are thin vertical flat plates affixed to a wing. They work best when they wraparound the leading edge. A good fence design is 10% of the chord in height on top and extends back to 40% of the chord size. On the underside extend it to just the front 10% of the chord. Make the height in front and underneath just 5% of the chord.

A fence on top of a wing prevents inflow due to the lower air pressure towards the center of the wing. Similarly, a fence on the bottom prevents air outflow.

Fences are placed in one or more locations along the wingspan depending on the goals of the designer. A useful location to place a fence is right in front of the inner edge of the ailerons. It will help to maintain their effectiveness in a stall.

5.5. Washout

Washout is a twist put on a wing to improve its stalling characteristics. There are two types of washout, structural and aerodynamic. It is very common for both types to be used at the same time on one wing.

Wings with high taper ratios (the wing tip chord is less than half the root chord) or significant sweepback are prone to tip stalling. This means that a stall starts at the wing tip and then progresses to the rest of the wing. The problem is that both wingtips are never going to start stalling at the same moment. So invariably one wing drops, you lose aileron effectiveness, and you are at risk of entering a spin. Bad stuff.

Structural washout decreases the angle of attack at the tips. The wings are physically twisted. When you look at the wing, the trailing edge is raised at the tips compared to the trailing edge at the wing root.

Aerodynamic washout uses a different airfoil at the tip that stalls at a higher angle of attack than the root airfoil. For example, if the root airfoil is 15% thick, use an airfoil that is 12% thick at the tips.

Don't overdo it. About 3 degrees of washout should be enough in most cases. Washout also doesn't have to be applied uniformly along the wingspan. It's fine if you put the twist (either structural or aerodynamic) only on the outer half of each wing.

Washout will not affect the stability of the model. It will negatively affect the overall efficiency and the top speed of the model, since the wingtips might end up flying at a negative angle of attack at high speeds.

5.6. Wingtips

The first airplane to fly with winglets was Burt Rutan's VariEze (see Figure 5.8 on page 102). Winglets look great on a wing. Every airplane should have winglets. Go ahead, put some on.

Well, I wish it were that easy. In truth, adding winglets should be an action of last resort. Really.

At best a winglet reduces the wing's drag an amount equivalent to extending the wing length by 1/3 the winglet height. Testing by NASA showed a 4% decrease in wing drag. That's not much! And designing an efficient winglet is not easy, so chances are very good that your homebrewed design will be far less effective. In fact, your winglet design is more likely to make the performance worse than to improve it. So why in the world do so many full-size airplanes have winglets? Well, there are usually other reasons that lead to this solution.

If the wingspan of the airplane must be limited for some reason, then adding winglets is the only way to decrease the wing loading. I'm talking about airplanes that are already in production where completely replacing the wing is not an option. This is a problem shared by a lot of commercial airliners that need to fit into existing airport gates. Stretch versions of these airplanes are common, and if you want to maintain the climb rate, then adding winglets is usually the only solution.

The most popular competition classes for full-size sailplanes limit the wingspan to 15 meters (49 feet). Adding winglets is an easy way to increase the glider's performance.

Winglets do have one advantage over extending the wingspan. For a wingtip lengthening that works as well as a given winglet, the winglet will only have half the wing root bending moment. The weight penalty will probably be higher, though. In the case of an existing airplane where you don't have the luxury of redesigning the wing, adding winglets looks like a mighty attractive option.

There are other reasons besides aerodynamic efficiency for tacking on winglets. Don't under estimate their marketing value! Even in some commercial airliners, where fuel economy is paramount, it is believed that winglets were added mainly to increase the sex appeal of the aging airliner in the eyes of the passengers. Putting winglets on a model airplane can also help a lot with its visibility.

Many pilots report improved aileron effectiveness at slow speeds with winglets. This is because of the improved air flow around the tips. If your design wallows around and has very sluggish aileron control at slow speeds, add winglets and tell your friends you did it because they look cool.

Winglets work better when they are blended into the wingtip. This means that, when looked at from the front, the end of the wing curves up smoothly and turns into the winglet. They should also be toed-in to account for spanwise air flow. Use 2 degrees for an unswept wing, 5 degrees for a highly swept design.

A recent development is raked (see Figure 5.4 on the facing page) or crescent-shaped wingtips (see Figure 5.5 on the next page), where the sweep angle grows progressively larger towards the tips. NASA tested as much as a 5.5% drag reduction with crescent-shaped wingtips. Raked tips lower the drag and increase the lift available for takeoff and climb. Winglets only decrease the drag. Some airliners are beginning to incorporate this design instead of winglets. Making the tips strong enough to avoid flutter may be a challenge (see Section 6.4 on page 121).

Wing tip and planform design are areas of very active research nowadays. We still have much to learn (see Figure 5.6 on page 100).

Thinking about wing tip *plates*? These are thin flat sheets attached to the end of each wing. Well, they better be twice as long (front to back) as the wing root chord, otherwise their net effect will be a losing proposition.

A wingtip design that manages to lower induced drag might actually increase the separation drag. That is the case with a completely squared-off wingtip. To visualize this design, imagine the end of the wing sheared off cleanly at a 90 degree vertical angle.

A squared off rear end of the wingtip tends to decrease induced drag but it increases separation drag. It decreases induced drag because the tip vortices are kept far apart. It increases separation drag because the tips are not as streamlined as with a conventional wingtip. This is a good trade-off at very low wing aspect ratios, such as those that are less than two, that already suffer from very high induced drag.

At a minimum, round the front corners of the tips (as seen from above) and taper the underside to meet up with the top at a sharp angle (as seem from the front). Keep the rear of the wingtips square. This is basically what a Hörner tip is (see Figure 5.7 on page 100), and it'll improve the wing performance slightly.

Don't worry too much about this one. A bad wing tip design reduces the wing's effective span by about 20% of the tip chord. A Hörner tip only reduces the effective wingspan by about 10% of the tip chord. If the tip chord

Figure 5.4. Raked wing
This commuter airliner has raked wingtips for higher performance.

Figure 5.5. Crescent-shaped moon
A crescent is a half-ellipse inside a half-circle with their axes aligned.

Figure 5.6. Flying bird
An Osprey doing what it does best. Someday we might reach his efficiency
with our airplane designs.

Figure 5.7. Hörner wing tip

is 5 inches (12.7 centimeters), then the difference in effective wingspan is just one inch (2.5 centimeters).

5.7. Multiple Wings

A tandem wing airplane has two wings in tandem of roughly the same size and no tail. If the front wing is significantly smaller, then we call that a canard (see Figure 5.8 on the next page). If the rear wing is significantly smaller, we call that a lifting stabilizer.

There are two types of canards in use. The traditional type, like the VariEze, uses the canard surface like an additional wing. A newer type of canard aircraft uses the canard surface strictly as a control surface, not as a lifting surface (see Figure 5.9 on the following page). I do not consider these newer types true canards, since they only have one lifting wing.

Biplanes and triplanes (see Figure 5.10 on page 103) are technically multi--wing designs. But since their wings are very close to each other and they have horizontal stabilizer, they are more like conventional aircraft.

5.7.1. History

During the early dawn of aviation 200 years ago, nobody knew how an airplane was supposed to look. Many ideas were tried and discarded. These ideas were often inspired from observing birds in flight. The Wright brothers made all of their early designs canards, with the tail in front. Was aerodynamic efficiency foremost in their minds? Hardly. They were much more concerned about their butts. You see, a few years earlier another aviation pioneer, Otto Lilienthal, had crashed and died while flying one of his designs. The Wrights had no desire to duplicate his fate, and so they put the tail in front as a sort of "crush zone" for their airplanes.

The idea of using two wings, one in front of the other, goes back to Thomas Walker, who published the first design in 1831. The configuration was later popularized by Samuel Pierpont Langley, a contemporary of the Wright brothers. In fact, tandem wing aircraft used to be called the "Langley type".

Figure 5.8. Rutan VariEze
An innovative homebuilt design.   The first airplane design ever with winglets.

Figure 5.9. Eurofighter Typhoon
The small forward canard surface is not for producing lift but only for controlling the aircraft.

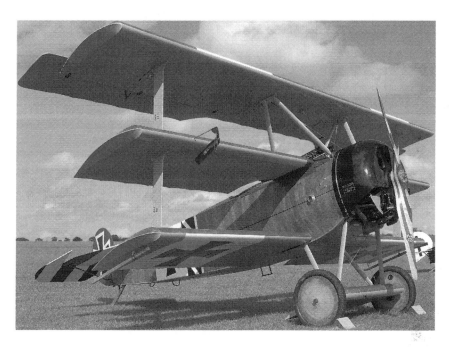

Figure 5.10. Fokker Triplane
Famous for the Red Baron, though he only made 20 of his 80 kills with it.
A flawed design, it had great maneuverability (and drag!).

Langley only managed to fly his tandem wing model, since his full-size airplanes were complete failures. Langley's research focus was the propulsion system. Being much better funded than the Wright brothers, his engine had a much better power to weight ratio. But the Wright brother's focus was controllability and sound aerodynamics, which in the end proved to be the key to success. Interestingly, the Wright brothers did not want an airplane that was too stable. They wanted the pilot to be in control at every moment.

The first full-size tandem wing airplane to fly was built by Louis Peyret in 1907. An unpowered glider, it managed to break the duration record at the time with a flight lasting 3 hours and 22 minutes. Later his pilot broke the record again with a flight lasting over eight hours.

Given this early success, why weren't more of the early designs canards or tandem airplanes? Was it because the other designers felt that putting the tail in the back was more efficient? Nope. They were concerned about saving their butts, too—as in saving their butts from getting sued by the Wright brothers. The Wrights believed that the best use of the airplane was as a tool to avoid war. They felt that it could be used to prevent surprise attacks, and therefore their main focus in the early years was to secure a contract from the United States Army. They were extremely protective of their ideas, delaying for years their first public demonstration flight until they had been granted their aviation patents. Afterwards, they did not hesitate to sue any competitor that they felt was infringing on their patents. As a way of avoiding an expensive legal battle, most competitors simply put the tail in the back.

A famous tandem wing airplane was named the Flying Flea by its designer, Henri Mignet. The Flea (see Figure 5.11 on the facing page) first took to the air in 1934 (sorry, I couldn't resist saying that). A very poor pilot himself, Mignet designed the Flea to be very easy to fly. Mignet published a book containing the plans and instructions. Some call this the first home-built airplane. It has recently become popular again, with new Flying Fleas being built all over the world.

In 1977 Burt Rutan designed the Quickie, another tandem wing airplane (see Figure 5.12 on page 106). Rutan has said that the design was inspired by

Figure 5.11. Mignet Flying Flea (Pou-du-Ciel)

the X-wing fighters from the movie Star Wars, released the same year. With just an 18 HP (13.5 kW) engine, they can cruise at over 110 mi/h (175 km/h).

Typical contest rules for free flight models do not count the area of the horizontal stabilizer towards the total wing area. This is what led to the popularity of lifting stabilizers on these models. Tailless designs are penalized by these rules, which is why they are rarely seen.

5.7.2. Disadvantages

Why is the tandem wing or canard configuration not more popular today? Great question! I'm not sure. Part of the problem is that it looks different. Very different. Some, horror of horrors, have called it ugly.

Aerodynamically, the main problem mentioned in the literature is that the front wing interferes with the rear wing. Both canard and tandem wing aircraft suffer from this. First, the rear wing is flying through the disturbed air that is left behind the front wing. Second, the front wing pushes the air down, forcing the rear wing to have higher induced drag. The rear wing is typically penalized 20% as far as its lift producing ability. The tail of a conventional airplane suffers from a similar problem, but in that case you are losing control effectiveness and not lift.

Induced drag is proportional to the square of the lift coefficient of the wing. If you have two wings, each generating half the lift, in theory you have cut the induced drag in half. In practice, the front wing is more highly loaded so

Figure 5.12. Rutan Quickie

its induced drag will not be half of the original single wing. Also, the aspect ratio of the tandem wings would have to be twice that of the original single wing. Due to bending loads, this rarely happens in practice.

Because they have two wings, building a tandem wing airplane can be more expensive. The wings will also put extra torsional loads on the fuselage.

Canards were once believed to be safer than ordinary airplanes because of their stall resistance. Stall spin accidents continue to be a leading cause of aviation accidents. But their highly loaded canard surface leads to faster landing speeds. In reality, the overall accident rate for canards is higher, though the fatality rate is lower (as compared to conventional configuration aircraft).

The size of the canard surface is critical for good performance and it is easy to get it wrong. In other words, it is easy to design a bad canard airplane.

Canard surfaces and lifting stabilizers are relatively small. This makes them inefficient lift producers. Due to their small size and the need to stall after the main wing, canard surfaces tend to have high aspect ratios. This lowers their Reynolds numbers.

Adding flaps to a multiple wing design is a challenge. The center of gravity is always near the front wing. That makes the wing loading of the front wing much higher than the rear wing. It also puts the rear wing far away from the center of gravity, giving it a much longer lever arm.

All of these factors combine to make flaps on the rear wing much more effective than flaps on the front wing. In practice their movement would have to be coordinated across both wings. Creating a mechanical linkage in a full-size airplane to do this is difficult and would add weight. With our modern computer radios we could program the special movement, but it would still be tricky to get right.

5.7.3. Advantages

Tandem wing airplanes are stall-resistant for the same reason that canard airplanes are stall resistant. The front wing is designed to stall first, triggering a nose drop that immediately restores lift to the main wing. That is the reason Rutan chose a canard configuration for his famous VariEze and Long-Eze homebuilt designs. However, the front wing in a tandem design typically carries about 60% of the weight. So stalls are still possible, but perhaps not as severe as on a conventional design.

Like canards, tandem-winged airplanes are all lift. There is no horizontal tail pushing down. But unlike the highly loaded canard surface, the front wing in a tandem airplane still permits relatively slow stall and landing speeds.

Since they have two lifting surfaces set far apart, tandem-winged airplanes are naturally more stable than a conventional airplane. This gives you more flexibility in where you can put the center of gravity. This also frees up the center section of the fuselage for carrying cargo.

Canards and lifting stabilizers contribute to the lift, so their main wings can be made about 20% smaller than on a conventional configuration.

5.8. Tailless

The only cargo carried by a model is the power system and radio components, and these usually don't take up a lot of space. The wing is the only part of an airplane that you *must* have. Why not get rid of everything else?

Tailless airplanes are very clean and they like to fly fast. Building light is critical for good performance. A tailless design has about a 15% higher lift-to-drag ratio at a 35% higher speed. They also have a 15% worse sink rate which occurs at a faster speed, too.

Forward swept flying wings are very rare due to the many stability and efficiency problems inherent in the design. If the tailless design has no sweep, it is called a plank because that's what it looks like. A plank is very easy to build, but a back-swept (normally just called swept) flying wing has the potential for higher performance.

5.8.1. History

The first successful powered tailless airplane was the Dunne D.5 from England which first flew in 1910 (see Figure 5.13 on the following page). His aircraft were very stable. Unfortunately, they were too stable to meet military needs for maneuverability. Due to ill health and lack of interest by the military, he was done with his designs by 1913 (pun intended).

The first production tailless airplane was the Messerschmitt Me 163 from 1941 (see Figure 5.14 on page 111), which also holds the distinction of being the only rocket powered fighter ever. It was designed by the German Alexander Lippisch during World War II. Lippisch created many tailless designs, building flying models first to test his ideas. It had amazing performance, being able to climb to 40,000 feet (12,000 meters) in only three minutes. The tremendous speed worked against it, reaching and passing the target in a matter of seconds. Ultimately, the design proved more hazardous to its pilots than to the enemy.

There is much, much more to the history of tailless aircraft. For an extensive account, visit the Century of Flight website[1].

5.8.2. Twist

Swept tailless airplanes require twist in their wings for pitch stability. This is normally done using a combination of geometric and aerodynamic washout (see Section 5.5 on page 95). Planks should only have a small amount of twist, if any.

Walter Panknin with the help of Helmut Schenk developed a fantastic formula for determining the required amount of wing twist for stability in a tailless design (5.10 on the next page). It applies equally well to aft swept, plank, and forward swept designs and is known to be accurate for sweep angles of up to 30 degrees. For a delta wing, use a taper ratio of zero. It should be apparent that less twist is needed when there is a higher aspect ratio or more sweep.

---

[1]www.century-of-flight.net

Figure 5.13. Dunne Tailless Biplane
This is a military version. I guess they used harsh language on the enemy?

$$Twist_{geom} = \frac{(K_1 * C_{Mroot} + K_2 * C_{Mtip}) - C_L * St}{1.4 * 10^{-5} * aspectRatio^{1.43} * sweepAngle}$$
$$- (\alpha_{L=0root} - \alpha_{L=0tip})$$
$$K_1 = \frac{(3 + 2 * taperRatio + taperRatio^2)}{4 * (1 + taperRatio + taperRatio^2)}$$
$$K_2 = 1 - K_1 \tag{5.10}$$
$$C_M = \text{moment coefficient}$$
$$\alpha_{L=0} = \text{zero lift angle}$$
$$C_L = \text{wing design lift coefficient}$$
$$St = \text{Use 0.05 here. For a trainer 0.10 is better.}$$

Tailless designs without sweep (planks) require airfoils with positive moment coefficients. This is the tendency of the airfoil to pitch up or down. Swept flying wings work better with moment coefficients close to zero. Symmetrical airfoils meet this criteria, but they are not very good lift producers.

Figure 5.14. Messerschmitt Me 163 Komet

Like the tail in a conventional design, the wing tips in a tailless swept wing may also be pushing down for stability. If that is the case, consider using an inverted (upside-down) airfoil at the tips. Note that this may not be a very efficient design.

Putting most of the twist in the wing center section is definitely a bad idea. Putting the twist uniformly along the span makes construction easier, especially if a foam cutter is used. It is better if most of the twist is at the tips.

A good design for an aft swept flying wing uses a center section with a high lift airfoil with close to zero moment coefficient, and no twist. Fences mark the boundary of the center section. Put 1/3 of the required wing twist in the middle third of the wingspan. Put the remaining 2/3 of the required twist in the outer 1/3 of the wings. 20 degrees of sweep is usually about right.

5.8.3. Disadvantages

All airplane wings develop the most lift in their center sections. If the wing is tapered and swept, turbulence can develop there because of crossflow. The fuselage in a conventional airplane tends to tame this turbulence. The Horten brothers used a "duck tail" in many of their designs to combat this. This is an increase of the chord size towards the wing center, giving the center section a diamond shape. The 1/4 chord line of the wings should meet at less than a 180 degree angle (forward sweep at the center). This means that the sides of the duck tail should meet at a sharper angle at the back than the leading edges do at the front. Another option is to lower the sweep or taper in the center. Wing fences (see Section 5.4.1 on page 94) can also be used to combat this effect.

Planks are not a good choice for an aerobatic airplane since they can be sluggish to turn. They also require large vertical stabilizers since their moment arm is so short.

5.8.4. Advantages

The opposite of tandem-winged aircraft, tailless are less expensive to build due to their lack of tail surfaces or a fuselage.

Planks make great slope gliders. They are very sturdy and can easily handle high winds and gusts.

Planks also make great trainers. They are very stable and can survive bad landings. A plank glider will also be very stable while thermalling.

5.8.5. Airfoil Recommendations

For a plank you want an airfoil with a positive moment coefficient, but not too high. A great choice is the EMX-07 (see Figure 5.15).

Swept wings work better with airfoils that have close to zero moment coefficients and decent maximum lift coefficient. A great choice would be the MH45 (see Figure 5.16 on the following page).

Figure 5.15. EMX-07 airfoil
9.9% thick, 2.5% camber, 0.01 moment coefficient.

Figure 5.16. MH45 airfoil
9.8% thick, 1.6% camber, -0.006 moment coefficient.

6. Airplanes

6.1. Stability

Since an airplane flies in three dimensional space, it should make sense that it has to be stable along three axes.

Having too much stability along any one of these axes is almost as bad as having too little stability. Either way you'll have a model that doesn't want to go where **you** want it to go.

How much stability you need depends on many factors such as the pilot skill, how fast you are flying, and what you are trying to do at the time.

This is one area that still manages to surprise big time airplane designers once in a while, so don't feel bad if you don't get it right the first time.

Here are some rough guidelines for coming up with a hopefully reasonable stability margin for your maiden flight. The good news here is that even if the stability isn't quite right, chances are that the model will still be flyable. It just may not be much fun to fly until you fix the problem. The other bit of good news is that you can test your guess by performing power-off uncontrolled glides.

Tail control surfaces are often required to operate at high angles of attack. This calls for an airfoil that is stall resistant and efficient (see Figure 6.1 on the next page). For an aerobatic airplane, a thicker airfoil like NACA 0018 would work even better.

6.1.1. Up and Down

Longitudinal (pitch) stability is affected by the horizontal stabilizer and is adjusted by where the center of gravity is located on the airplane.

Figure 6.1. NACA 0012 airfoil
A 12% thick airfoil that is a great choice for tail surfaces.

In a conventional aft-tail configuration, a good place to put the center of gravity is 30% back from the leading edge of the mean aerodynamic chord (MAC). For a trainer, make it 25%.

The MAC is the average wing chord size. The MAC location is just a fancy way of saying where the average position of the wing's chord lies when you account for wing sweep and taper. On a rectangular wing planform, the MAC is just the wing chord and the MAC location is halfway out the wingspan. A wing with a simple taper and a taper ratio that is not too low has a MAC that is the a little bigger than the average of the root and tip chords and a MAC location that is a little closer to the root than halfway out the wingspan. You can use (6.1) to compute these values for a tapered wing, but I won't get upset if you just take a good look at your wing and guess.

$$MAC_{size} = \frac{2}{3} * (C_{root} + C_{tip} - \frac{C_{root} * C_{tip}}{C_{root} + C_{tip}})$$

$$MAC_{location} = \frac{1}{3} * (\frac{C_{root} + 2 * C_{tip}}{C_{root} + C_{tip}})$$

$$C = \text{chord size}$$

$$MAC_{location} = (0.0 = \text{root}, 1.0 = \text{tip})$$

(6.1)

In canard and tandem-wing designs, you need to find the MAC size and location of each lifting surface and then take a weighted average based of their respective wing areas. Then use 30% of the resulting MAC to locate where the center of gravity belongs. Yes, it's as simple as that sounded.

These calculations are approximate, since there are many factors that affect the results. Conducting power-off gliding tests is always prudent.

Not normally a big deal, but keep in mind that for every one MAC that the propeller is ahead of the center of gravity, the static longitudinal stability is reduced by 2%.

As an airplane design is revised, it always tends to get heavier and for the center of gravity to migrate towards the tail. Both of these are bad news. Get into the habit of weighing your model often and checking the center of gravity after every non-trivial change.

6.1.2. Turning

Directional or yaw stability is affected by the vertical stabilizer and adjusted by the location of the center of gravity.

It's easy to cheat on this one. Just put a big vertical tail on the model and then start cutting it down in size until the model becomes directionally unstable. Done!

Here's a method that's not too hard to follow. Create a cardboard cutout of the side profile of the model. Double the thickness of the cardboard wherever there are more than two horizontal surfaces such as the wing. At the wings, layer one additional piece of cardboard for each wing half of the proper size to account for the wing sweep and dihedral. Find the center of gravity (CG) of the cardboard. This is your center of lateral area (CLA).

Measure the distance between the vertical tail MAC and the model's center of gravity. This is your vertical tail moment arm (VTMA). The CLA should be 25% of the VTMA back from the CG.

Wing dihedral and sweep both contribute to directional stability. It's unusual for a model to be directionally unstable and stable along the other two axes for this reason. In other words, if the model is stable in pitch and in roll, it is probably also stable in yaw.

6.1.3. Side to Side

Lateral or roll stability is affected by many factors (6.2). D_{tip} is the shape of the wing tip. Upturned tips such as a Hörner design get a bonus of one extra degree of effective dihedral. Generally speaking you will have more effective dihedral with higher wing locations, winglets, and more sweep.

$$Dihedral_{tot} = 87 * t * (\frac{C_L * \tan Sw}{3} + \frac{k * D_{geoRad}}{6})$$

$$+ D_{tip} + D_{pos} + D_{geo} + \frac{20 * h_w}{s}$$

$$k = \frac{5.7}{1 + \frac{2}{AR}}$$

$$t = \frac{1 + 2TR}{1 + TR}$$

$$AR = \text{aspect ratio}$$

$$TR = \text{taper ratio} \tag{6.2}$$

$$C_L = \text{lift coefficient}$$

$$Sw = \text{sweep angle, measured at 50\% chord}$$

$$D_{geoRad} = \text{geometric dihedral in radians (small angles)}$$

$$D_{tip} = \text{(1=upturned tips,-1=downturned tips)}$$

$$D_{pos} = \text{(5.5=high wing,-5.5=low wing)}$$

$$D_{geo} = \text{geometric dihedral}$$

$$h_w = \text{winglet height}$$

$$s = \text{semi-span, wingspan/2}$$

The goal is to have about six degrees of total dihedral for the model's wing. Wings without ailerons need about twice as much. Ten degrees of sweep (measured at the 25% chord line) is generally equivalent to one degree of dihedral, but the formula will be more accurate.

On a polyhedral wing, you have to take a weighted average, based on the distance from the centerline, of the amount of dihedral on each wing panel to find the effective dihedral.

Of the three axes of stability, this is the hardest one to predict on paper. There are just too many factors that influence it. Dutch roll is a periodic oscillation that involves yaw and roll and can occur if there is too much dihedral or too little vertical stabilizer area. Conversely, too little dihedral or too large a vertical stabilizer can lead to spiral divergence, where the model enters a death spiral without any control inputs.

6.2. Control Surfaces

You'll lose about 20% of the effectiveness of a control surface if the hinge gap is not sealed. So seal them! There are many ways of doing this. 3M Blenderm surgical tape, iron-on heat shrink film, laminating film, etc.

All moving tails (horizontal or vertical) are very effective, but they tend to be heavier than a conventional hinged tail.

Set each half of a V tail at 45 degrees. The area of a V tail will need to be the same as a conventional tail, so it'll weigh about the same. You are going to have problems with control coupling, such as when using the elevator you get some yaw. The only practical advantage (besides good looks) I can think of is that it helps keep the tail away from the ground and out of harm's way during takeoffs and landings.

T tails are slightly more efficient, but you'll end up making the vertical stabilizer heavier and complicating the control linkage. They are also prone to being blanketed by the wing during a stall.

It's usually a bad idea to extend the ailerons all the way out to the wing tips. First of all, they won't be very effective due to the vortex at the tip. They are more likely to get damaged if the wing tip hits the ground, and they can lead to flutter (see Section 6.4 on page 121). To be safe, go out no more than 90% of the wing span.

The hinged surfaces (elevator, ailerons, flaps, and rudder) are most *efficient* when they are 25% of the chord width. But their efficiency is good in the 17% to 40% range. They are more *effective* the wider they are. Therefore, 40% of the chord width is a good choice for the tail and flaps. With ailerons, you want to minimize their effect on the wing's ability to produce lift, so 20% is a prudent choice here.

You'll never need more than 45 degrees of deflection on any of them (except flaps). You don't need to make the rudder very tall, since it gets a 50% boost in effective aspect ratio from having the elevator at its base.

6.2.1. Horizontal Stabilizers

Design canard and conventional tails with twice the aspect ratio of the main wing and with 30% of its span for best efficiency. The higher aspect ratio combats the detrimental effects of their lower Reynolds numbers.

You are more likely to need a strong force to do up elevator than down. For example, to recover from a dive. Since pushrods are stronger in tension, there is an argument to be made to require a pulling force on the pushrod to pull the elevator up.

6.2.2. Flaps

Slow flying model airplanes don't need flaps. Keep it simple.

The takeoff roll is proportional to lift-off speed squared. So increasing the amount of lift generated by the wings even by a little bit can measurably shorten the takeoff roll. For takeoffs, the idea is to increase the lift without increasing the drag too much. A good compromise is to use 15 degrees of flaps.

A nice goal in an airplane design is to make the take-off roll and the landing roll the same length. For landings, you want as much drag as your airplane can handle. How much it can handle depends on how much power is available for a go-around. In an emergency situation, you are probably going to forget to raise your flaps. By raising the flaps you also suddenly lose their extra lift when you might be close to the ground. So make sure that your airplane can still climb under full power and full flaps. If this is not a concern (like in a glider), then use 90 degree landing flaps. Otherwise start experimenting with something like 45 degrees.

6.3. Trailing Edges

Don't lose too much sleep over the trailing edges. Yes, they can make a difference in the performance, but building a good one is not too hard. The key is not to fall for the myth of the razor sharp trailing edge. They are difficult to build, prone to breaking, and are simply not needed.

A much better solution is a squared-off trailing edge. For best results keep the thickness at less than 0.5% of the chord length. That is not much. On a 10 inch wing chord (25 centimeters), that is less than 1/16 inch (1.25 millimeters). It'll still work if it is thicker than that, so do your best.

Don't round it off in any way! The 90 degree turns are what make it work. The air will roll off the end of the wing or stabilizer and just keep on moving straight.

6.4. Flutter

About ten years ago I used to fly a very lightweight handlaunched balsa glider. In those days all we knew was javelin launches. The wings were very thin, and I was constantly fixing it up. After a few crash/repair cycles, the wings developed a severe flutter problem. On every hard launch, they would flap like a bird. I continued flying it anyway, more out of wonderment than anything else.

Wings, stabilizers, and control surfaces can all suffer from flutter. Due to their nature, aerobatic airplanes, large gliders, and swept flying wings are more prone to flutter than other designs.

Flutter is a self-starting natural vibration that can quickly lead to self-destruction. The stiffer a structure is, the higher in frequency are its natural modes of vibration. The most destructive modes of vibration are in the lower frequencies because they have greater amplitude.

The center of lift of an airfoil is approximately at the 25% chord point. This is the point where the lift appears to be concentrated. The problem is that the center of mass is usually further back than that. So when flutter develops, it leads to severe twisting forces.

Note that I'm talking about the center of mass of the structure, not of the entire aircraft. For a wing, I'm talking about the balance point of the wing by itself.

The usual way to combat flutter is to make the entire structure stiffer. Tried and true, but it quickly leads to much added weight. A smarter approach is to add weight to the front of the structure to bring the center of mass in line with the center of lift. This will increase the structure's natural mode of vibration, making it harder to start a flutter, and it will also make it better able to withstand its effects. Even if you don't completely line up the two, just getting them closer will improve the situation.

Control surface flutter is rarer in model airplanes that fly at typical speeds. To avoid it, balance a control surface on its hinge line. Control surfaces can also experience flutter prematurely if they are mounted loosely. Make sure the hinges and pushrod connections are tight.

Every model airplane has a critical airspeed where flutter is guaranteed to occur. Please take reasonable precautions to make that speed as high as possible.

6.5. Wing incidence

The wing incidence is the angle that the wing root makes to the rest of the airplane. The goal is to have the fuselage be perfectly horizontal at the design cruise speed. That will yield the most efficient design. Watch out that this does not result in a tail strike when you come in for a landing!

Reflexed flaps (flaps which move up to a negative angle) can be used to help keep the fuselage horizontal as the model speeds up.

6.6. Scale Effects

The physical laws governing the scaling of a 3D object like a model airplane are well understood (see Figure 6.1 on the next page). These are the formulas used by RCadvisor's calculator, so you may be better off just taking advantage of the calculator.

The percentages in the table are all relative to the full-size airplane. Let's use a Piper Super Cub as an example (see Figure 6.2 on page 125). We'll pretend we are building a 1/8 scale model.

The fully loaded Cub weighs 1750 pounds (794 kg). Our model needs to weigh 3.5 pounds (1.6 kg). The original's wingspan is 35 feet (11 m). The model's wingspan will be 4.5 feet (1.4 m). The Cub flies at 120 miles/hour (180 km/h). Our model needs to fly at 42 miles/hour (63 km/h). And so on.

Building a scale model as light as called for in the table is a real challenge. If you end up making the model heavier (almost inevitable), make sure the thrust to weight ratio and the wing loading are still appropriate, even if you have to make the wing a little bigger.

The "internal clock" of the model will always be faster than the full-size airplane. Don't worry about it. The goal is to have scale appropriate behavior, even if the model appears to be moving too fast. The fast clock might be of benefit for models that spectators are expecting to fly fast (see Figure 6.3 on page 125).

Since the internal clock of a model slows down as it gets bigger, be careful not to try and fly a scaled-up version at the same *apparent* speed as a smaller sibling.

For quick calculations and comparisons between models, a simplified formula can come in handy (6.3 on page 126). This formula works better than the "wing cubed loading" formula which you may have heard of. The airplane type constant will be the same for different scale sizes of the same model. This number will also be very similar to the value for other models of the same type (trainer, sport, glider, aerobatic, etc).

Scale factor	Weight (%)	Wing span (%)	Wing loading (%)	Power (%)	RPM (%)	Thrust (%)	Airspeed (%)	Force damping (%)	Time (%)
n	n^3	n	n	$n^{3.5}$	$\frac{1}{\sqrt{n}}$	n^3	$\sqrt{n}$	n^2	$\sqrt{n}$
$\frac{1}{4}$	1.56	25	25	0.78	200	1.56	50	6.25	50
$\frac{1}{5}$	0.80	20	20	0.36	224	0.80	45	4.00	45
$\frac{1}{6}$	0.46	17	17	0.19	245	0.46	41	2.78	41
$\frac{1}{8}$	0.20	13	13	0.07	283	0.20	35	1.56	35
$\frac{1}{9}$	0.14	11	11	0.05	300	0.14	33	1.23	33
$\frac{1}{10}$	0.10	10	10	0.03	316	0.10	32	1.00	32
$\frac{1}{12}$	0.06	8	8	0.02	346	0.06	29	0.69	29

Table 6.1. Scale factors

Figure 6.2. Piper Super Cub

Figure 6.3. Model warplane
Model warplanes are supposed to fly fast, so their faster internal clock rates might be of benefit.

$$airplaneTypeConstant = \frac{airplaneWeight}{wingArea * wingSpan} \quad (6.3)$$

There are other factors that conspire to make the smaller models poorer flyers than the bigger ones. As a proportion of the total weight, the radio gear is a much bigger fraction in the smaller models. As we have seen, Reynolds number effects cause higher drag and lower maximum lift on the smaller wings.

The control responsiveness and the stability of a model airplane change as the square of the wingspan. This is because of the much lower mass and resultant lower force damping in the smaller model. This means that it will respond more quickly to the control inputs and it will be less stable. Adjust the design accordingly.

6.7. Visibility

Any airplane that is difficult to see is bound to be a poor flyer, simply because you won't do a very good job of controlling it.

Start with your sunglasses. Most sunglasses are made for drivers and their primary function is to cut down on road glare. The typical grass or even paved flying field does not have a glare problem.

Yellow tinted sunglasses work really well against glare but they hide colors. This is important visual information that you are throwing away. You will also be masking away the high frequency colors such as blue. High frequency colors are easier to see. Get instead some gray tinted sunglasses. The colors will stay true, and your overall visual acuity will improve.

Use light colors. Epoxy resins cured at room temperature weaken at elevated temperatures. Keeping the battery cool is always a good idea. Visibility of light colors is better under most sunlight conditions.

Our eyes cannot see color when a small object gets far away. Two colors with the same brightness, such as bright red and bright blue, will blend into one at a distance. The key is to use light and dark colors. If you are not sure, load the color scheme into the computer and turn them all into grayscales.

We see shapes faster than colors. An excellent color scheme is to color the bottom of the wing a light color and to place four large dark colored circles on it. For the best visibility, make the circles orange. On top of the wing, use a broad sunburst pattern with light and dark colors. Do something similar with the horizontal stabilizer. Put a red stripe along the leading edge of the wing. That will contrast nicely against a blue sky or white clouds.

Draw a line on the side of the fuselage along the thrust line. Make the top a light color and the bottom a dark color.

6.8. Efficiency

How do you make sure you end up with an aerodynamically efficient design? Should you spend hours studying RCadvisor's airfoil database, until you find the perfect match for your design? No. In *decreasing* order of importance, here are three areas to focus on:

1. Minimize Zero Lift Drag Coefficient

2. Lower the Span Loading

3. Increase the Oswald Efficiency Factor

6.8.1. Minimize Zero Lift Drag Coefficient

The zero lift drag coefficient is the amount of drag that your entire airplane has when the wing is generating no lift. In other words, when the induced drag is zero. What's left? The skin friction drag and the separation drag. When the airplane is flying at high speed, the induced drag will be low and these two other remaining drag forces will be the main determining factors in the airplane's maximum speed.

Take a critical eye to your design. Is everything that is hanging out in the airstream teardrop shaped? A teardrop shape works best when it is about

3.5 times longer than wide. Even better, does it really need to be there in the first place? Do you really need to have a landing gear?

6.8.2. Lower the Span Loading

The span loading is the weight that the airplane wing has to carry per unit span. Normally it's a lot easier to increase the wingspan than to lower the weight, so you may want to think of this guideline as increasing the aspect ratio.

$$SpanLoading = \frac{airplaneWeight}{wingSpan} \qquad (6.4)$$

Lowering the span loading decreases the amount of lift per unit span that the wing has to generate. This means a reduced lift coefficient. A reduced lift coefficient means lower induced drag. In fact, the span loading is the primary factor in determining the induced drag of the wing. In practical terms this gives you shorter take-off and landing runs. You can also fly more slowly, which might be important depending on the aircraft's mission.

Making a wing longer generally increases its weight. Beyond a certain point, the increased weight offsets any reduction in drag. There are many factors that come into play here, but a useful rule of thumb is to keep the weight of the wing to $1/3^{rd}$ or less of the total airplane weight.

There is an interesting twist (pun intended) related to wing washout and span loading. On those wings that require washout, adding the required amount usually improves their span loading at cruise speeds. This means that leaving out the washout on a wing that requires it will usually lower its overall efficiency, rather than improve it.

6.8.3. Increase the Oswald Efficiency Factor

As an airplane pitches up to generate more lift, it produces more induced and separation drag. Every part of the airplane can contribute to this lift and drag, including the fuselage and tail. Some designs, such as the Wittman

Tailwind (see Figure 6.4 on the next page), generate a significant portion of their lift from the fuselage at cruise speeds.

The Oswald efficiency factor is a fraction normally in the range of 0.70 to 0.85. It is a measure of the efficiency of the airplane as a whole as a lift producing device. It is also called the span efficiency factor, though it is affected by the entire airplane and not just the wing. An elliptical wing planform without washout (twist) has long been considered to be the ideal.

By definition, the span efficiency of an elliptical wing without washout is 1. For many years it was believed to be the most efficient wing planform shape. Then in 1987 a scientist decided to revisit the question of maximum span efficiency by studying the crescent-shaped fins in animals such as dolphins using the advanced computers available at the time. Much to their surprise, they discovered that this shape has a span efficiency greater than 1 (see Figure 5.5 on page 99).

This may be counterintuitive, but increasing the wing aspect ratio decreases the Oswald factor. Going from an aspect ratio of 6 to an aspect ratio of 12 on a wing without sweep will decrease the Oswald factor by 20%. Why is that? It is harder for a tapered high aspect ratio wing to approach the span efficiency of an elliptical planform.

Think of the Oswald factor as the cost of producing lift. It is more important when the airplane is producing a lot of lift at slow speeds. Like the span loading, it helps determine the stall speed and the length of the take-off run.

Figure 6.4. Wittman Tailwind
Note the fuselage shaped like a very narrow (and low efficiency) wing.

7. Power Systems

7.1. Gas Engines

The first model airplane gas engines in the 1930s were a direct offshoot of motorcycle technology. They were all two-stroke (also called 2 cycle) and predominantly used spark ignitions. In 1947 glow engines were developed. Simpler, cheaper, and lighter than their predecessors, they soon took over the industry. Today glow two-stroke engines still dominate (see Figure 7.1 on the next page).

An alternative for many years that has never quite caught on is two-stroke diesel engines (see Figure 7.2 on the following page). Technically these are compression ignition engines, since true diesels inject the fuel after the air is compressed. Glow engines are sometimes called semi-diesels because their operation is so similar.

The key to high efficiency in an internal combustion engine is a high compression ratio. Diesels have an edge here, since they use compression to ignite the fuel/air mixture. They have very nice qualities such as lots of power, ease of use, high torque, and high efficiency. Unfortunately, their exhaust smells terrible. If you see me out flying at your field, please fly your model diesel downwind from me, OK?

Four-stroke (4 cycle) engines have become very popular lately (see Figure 7.3 on page 134). They sound better than two-stroke engines, are more economical, and produce more low-RPM torque. They use glow plugs that retain their heat during the extra cycles.

Like electric motors, their technology has improved significantly in recent years. Today, four-stroke engines and electric motors yield comparable power to glow engines for comparable weight. The weight of the engines

Figure 7.1. Two-stroke glow engines are the most popular gassers today.

Figure 7.2. Diesel engine. Note the screw on top for adjusting the compression ratio by moving the contra piston. A good choice if you can stand the smell.

and motors is comparable and the weight of the full gas tank is comparable to the batteries.

The most common fuel for model gas engines is methanol (methyl alcohol). Auto gasoline is used in some giant scale models, but at a penalty in the power/weight ratio. Nitromethane (nitro) is added to glow fuel to increase its ability to produce power.

Contrary to popular opinion, the fuel in an internal *combustion* engine *burns*. It does not explode. The heat from this combustion process is what indirectly leads to high cylinder pressures of about 300 psi (2,000 kPa) which push on the pistons.

Although the typical glow engine only extracts less than 20% of the energy contents in glow fuel as useful work, they are actually just as efficient as full-size airplane engines. Adding a tuned pipe muffler will boost the power even more.

Always run glow engines with a slightly rich gas/air mixture. It keeps the engine cooler and it'll last longer. Be careful with glow engines—they have been known to start without the battery being connected. It's the "semi-diesel" part of their behavior again.

When buying a new glow engine, pay close attention at the published specs. You want the peak horsepower of the engine to be at an RPM that you expect to be using. If it is too high, then the engine might not be a good fit for your application. If the manufacturer failed to provide this information, contact them and ask for it. A two-stroke glow engine is happier running at over 10k RPM, but you still want to swing a reasonably-sized propeller for better system efficiency.

Long stroke designs have taller cylinders and smaller pistons that move a longer distance in each stroke. Equal displacement engines have equal torque—the shape of the cylinder is not a factor. The location of the exhaust port is also not significant as far as the engine's ability to produce power.

Long stroke engines are taller, heavier, and prefer fuels high in nitro. The tradeoff is that they are quieter than short strokers (in other words, square designs) and are happier running low RPM applications.

Figure 7.3. Note the connecting rods in this four-stroke glow engine.

Full-size airplane gas engines are much more likely to rust their way out of service than to wear out. The same is true of our model gas engines, barring any bad crashes. Always keep the engine clean and well lubricated for longer life.

Gas engines differ in many ways from electric motors (see Table 7.1 on the following page). A crucial difference is that electric motors adjust their output torque depending on the load on their propeller shaft. Gas engines do not do this. Their torque is directly related to their RPM. This characteristic gives electric motors much more flexibility.

7.2. Batteries

Make sure you are using the latest battery technologies to power your model. LiPo, Molicel, and A123 cells are up to four times better than the technologies that preceded them (see Table 7.2 on the next page). Nominal voltage is the actual average voltage while the battery is being used in a typical application. Damage to the battery will occur if drained beyond the cutoff voltage.

There are two characteristics of batteries you should be familiar with. Energy density (energy/weight) is how efficient the battery is as a storage unit. Power density (power/weight) is how fast it can give it back. Despite the hype from the manufacturers, batteries of a given type are much more alike than different.

Make sure you are using a balancing charger. Their cost has dropped and their safety easily justifies any price difference.

The published specifications in a product catalog do a good job of summarizing the important data for a given battery. A brand-name battery is more likely to have better published specs and is also more likely to exceed those specs than an unknown brand.

If the manufacturer failed to supply the burst discharge rate, you can assume that a battery can sustain a discharge rate double the normal (or continuous) value for up to 30 seconds.

Gas Engines	Electric Motors
Lower up-front cost	Higher up-front cost
Higher operating cost	Lower operating cost
Easier to pick the right one	Harder to put a system together
Less power at high altitude	Doesn't care about altitude
Messy	Clean
Noisy	Quiet
Four-stroke sound very realistic	sound not so realistic
Limited flying locations	Many flying locations
More maintenance	Less maintenance
Break-in critical	No break-in needed

Table 7.1. Engine/Motor tradeoffs

	Nominal voltage	Cutoff voltage	Energy density
LiIonPo (LiPo)	3.7	3	4
LiIonPh (A123)	3.3	2	2.5
LiIonCo (Molicel)	3.8	2.5	2.5
NiMH	1.25	1	1
NiCd	1.25	1	1

Table 7.2. Battery Types. LiPo cells have *outstanding* energy density.

Batteries have internal resistance which causes the power losses to go up as the current goes up. The faster you drain the battery, the lower its capacity will appear. That is why battery capacities are measured at a discharge rate that would drain them in one hour.

Batteries do not like cold weather. The colder they get, the lower their capacity will appear. Try and keep them warm before you fly. They'll generate their own heat while in use.

To safely dispose of a LiPo battery (in other words, a liposuction), discharge the cells, cut off the wires, and immerse it in salt water for a week. After that they can just be tossed in the trash.

For radio transmitters (see Figure 7.4 on the following page) and receivers, the preferred battery technology today is NiMH cells. They are inexpensive and can take a decent amount of abuse. Some flyers of hand launched gliders have switched to using LiPos to power their airborne radio components. The voltage of two fully charged LiPos cells is a little too high for most receivers. Their solution is to add a micro voltage regulator to the mix.

7.2.1. A123 Cells

Electric model airplanes have been around for about three decades. A huge problem in the early days was battery energy density. In other words, they simply weighed too much for the amount of juice you could get out of them. This situation has improved dramatically in recent years with the advent of Lithium Ion Polymer (LiPo) cells, but a battery pack for a larger model can easily cost hundreds of dollars. The advent of hybrid gas/electric cars like the Toyota Prius has spurred an enormous amount of research into new battery technologies. There's an alternative to LiPos that offers intriguing possibilities.

A123 Systems[1] produces Lithium-Ion Nanophosphate cells. These cells have a nominal voltage of 3.3V and can withstand continuous discharge rates of 30C. This means that they can be safely discharged at a continuous 70 amp rate or 30 times their rated capacity. They can be safely discharged

---

[1] www.a123systems.com

Figure 7.4. Radio transmitters almost always use NiMH cells.

down to 2.0V. The voltage remains fairly constant through the discharge cycle, but they do have a sharp drop-off at the end. Expect 300 cycles before you notice any reduction in capacity while at 1000 cycles you'll have 75% of the original capacity. They are very safe. Overcharging or over discharging will not cause an explosion and will have little effect on the life of the battery. Balancing the cells when they are charged is still a good idea, but not absolutely required. They can be charged immediately after use in 15 minutes.

The cells are available in two sizes. The original M1 cell has a capacity of 2.3 Ah and weighs 70 grams (2.47 oz). A newer smaller size can hold 1.1 Ah and weighs 40 grams (1.41 oz).

The primary source for A123 M1 cells has been DeWalt 36 volt portable power tool battery packs. Each pack contains ten cells. I purchased two of these through EBay[2]. Single cells can also be purchased on-line from a growing variety of vendors. You can find two of the smaller cells in a Black & Decker VPX battery pack. The smaller cells can also be purchased separately.

There are many LiPo chargers that support or can be modified to support

---

[2] www. ebay. com

the charging of these A123 cells. Due to the sharp voltage drop-off when discharged, you are probably better off using a timer when you fly. Otherwise you need your electronic speed control to shut off the motor when 2.0V per cell is reached.

Bottom line? These cells give you 70% the energy density of LiPos for about 45% of the price. For many of us, that is a good trade-off. They are extremely safe and can be charged in 15 minutes. If you end up buying half as many battery packs because of the shorter charge time, then they become an even better value.

7.3. Electronic Speed Controllers

Nowadays electronic speed controllers (ESCs) are all pretty efficient and lightweight. Make sure the ESC gets plenty of cooling air and pay attention to the voltage and current limits.

Programmable controllers are the latest rage, but in most situations you don't need them. However, being able to set the cut-off voltage when you are using A123 cells can be handy.

The battery eliminator circuit (BEC) is what lets you power the receiver and servos from the motor's battery. Most BECs use linear voltage regulators, which are at most only about 40% efficient. With only two LiPo cells they are OK with up to four servos, but with three LiPos they become very inefficient and you better limit your setup to two servos.

On my smaller models, I almost always stick with two cell LiPo packs. Then I don't have to worry if I decide to build a four servo design.

There are BECs with switching voltage regulators that don't suffer from this limitation. But they are almost always separate units from the ESC, with the appropriate penalty in weight and cost.

A new trend is the use of high voltage (HV) battery packs for better overall power system efficiency. The required HV ESCs usually lack BECs.

7.4. Electric Motors

7.4.1. Types

Brushless motors are far superior to the older brushed ones. They are more efficient, last a lot longer, can spin a lot faster, require no maintenance, and can handle a much wider range of input power.

The first generation of brushless motors used speed controllers with shaft position sensors. Nowadays all brushless speed controllers are sensorless, since they are cheaper and they work just as well with model airplanes.

The term inrunner came into common use after outrunner motors started being used to power our model airplanes. An inrunner is a traditional style motor where the core rotates and the outside can is stationary. Compared to outrunner motors, inrunners have higher RPM and lower torque. Because of this, they are normally used with gearboxes. A coreless inrunner motor has no iron core, making them very efficient but they also have even lower torque than an inrunner with an iron stator.

In an outrunner electric motor, the core with the windings stays stationary and the outside can with the magnets spins. This is the opposite of an inrunner motor. Since the wire windings do not spin, commutation (the periodic switching of electrical current which causes the motor to spin) has to be done electronically as opposed to using brushes. This means that all outrunner motors are brushless. The primary advantage of outrunner motors is their lower RPM and greater torque which in most applications avoids the expense and weight of a gearbox.

7.4.2. Motor Constants

There are some good reasons why you might want to measure the constants of an electric motor you own. Due to variations in how the motor is wound and other manufacturing processes, no two motors are exactly alike. Some brands fail to provide this important information. You may have also wound the motor yourself, in which case you should confirm the quality of your winding job.

The published specifications for electric motors assume a motor temperature of 25°C (77°F). The standard operating temperature for model airplane motors is more like 50°C (122°F). As the temperature goes up, the electrical resistance in the windings increases and the magnets lose some of their strength. A good power system calculator (such as RCadvisor's) will take these changes into account. When measuring these constants, make sure the motor remains close to room temperature.

No Load Current

The no load current (I_0) is the current required to overcome frictional and related losses in a motor. To measure it, attach a multimeter to a motor and measure the current directly. Use a power source with a voltage that is close to what you expect to be cruising at. A good guess is $\frac{2}{3}$ of the nominal battery voltage.

Internal Resistance

The primary efficiency losses in an electric motor are due to electrical resistance in the copper windings. This energy manifests itself as heat.

There are a couple of good ways of measuring this internal resistance (R_m). Both methods require measuring the voltage and current going into the motor at the same time. You can use a multimeter and a simple device called a shunt, but my recommendation is to get one of the new on-board data loggers. These data loggers come in very handy for a multitude of different measurement tasks.

One method to measure the internal resistance involves applying a constant voltage and measuring both the voltage (V) and current (I) going through the motor. Using a simple formula (7.1) we can compute the motor winding's resistance.

$$InternalResistance = \frac{V}{I} \qquad (7.1)$$

A method I like better because it should be more accurate requires measuring the current, voltage and RPM of the motor at two points in the power curve. For best results, choose one data point at full power and the other at 50% throttle. Then use formula (7.2).

$$\mathrm{InternalResistance} = \frac{RPM_2 * V_1 - RPM_1 * V_2}{RPM_2 * I_1 - RPM_1 * I_2} \qquad (7.2)$$

Voltage Constant

The input voltage of a motor determines its RPM. This relationship is called the voltage constant (K_v). Once you know the internal resistance, it is easy to compute (7.3).

$$\mathrm{VoltageConstant} = \frac{RPM}{V - R_m * I} \qquad (7.3)$$

7.4.3. Thermal Capacity

As more electrical current is pumped through a motor, power losses increase and they manifest themselves primarily as heat. As the heat losses increase the efficiency decreases until all the extra input energy is going directly into excess heat. This is the motor's theoretical point of maximum power (7.4). In practice the motor may burn up before this point is reached.

$$\mathrm{Current}_{maxPower} = \frac{V + R_m * I_0}{2 * R_m} \qquad (7.4)$$

The absolute maximum current that a motor can draw occurs when the stator is kept from turning and the motor is fully stalled (7.5 on the next page). It will heat up quickly if you do this!

$$Current_{stall} = \frac{V}{R_m} \qquad (7.5)$$

How much cooling air a motor gets while it runs makes a big difference in its ability to dissipate heat. But there are a couple of rules of thumb that come in handy in estimating the power capacity of a given motor.

One rule says that an electric motor can safely handle 75 watts of power per ounce of motor weight (2.6 watts/gram). The other rule says to keep the power losses to less than 0.75 watts per square inch of motor surface area (0.12 watts/cm²).

Why are the rules in terms of power (watts) and not current? There is a direct inverse relationship between the torque produced by a motor and its RPM/volt speed. Normally the current losses dominate (7.6), but as the speed of the motor increases the voltage losses take over (7.7).

$$PowerLoss_{current} = I^2 * R_m \qquad (7.6)$$

$$PowerLoss_{voltage} = I_0 * V \qquad (7.7)$$

7.4.4. Windings

The copper wire in the motor core can be wound in different patterns. There are two primary ways of hooking up the wires together. These are called the Delta (Δ) and Wye (Y) winds. Only a few electric motors for model airplanes use a Delta wind. It is rarely used because it yields half the torque and double the RPM of the Wye wind.

The thickness of the wire used determines the number of times the wire can be wrapped around the core. Using a thinner wire so the number of winds can be doubled cuts the RPM in half and doubles the torque produced.

But the thinner wire will have greater resistance and will therefore result in higher heat losses.

Doubling the length of the stator cuts the RPM in half, doubles the torque and will also (as expected) double the power that can be produced.

7.4.5. Efficiency

I'm not aware of any motor manufacturers that have automated the process of winding the wire around the motor's core. If you want a quick feel for the build quality of a motor, take a peek inside. The best windings have the wire neatly organized so as to minimize the internal gaps (see Figure 7.5 on the facing page).

Rewinding a motor is not worth it to most of us. The sloppiest winding on the most inexpensive motor you can find won't be more than about 5% less efficient than an equivalent motor carefully hand wound.

Most of the power losses in an electric motor are due to the windings. Substituting higher quality magnets will improve the efficiency by at most 2.5%.

The maximum efficiency of a motor for a given input voltage is easy to calculate (7.8). To find the input voltage, multiply the number of input battery cells times their nominal voltage (see Table 7.2 on page 136). We can then compute the current (7.9) and RPM (7.10).

$$\text{Efficiency}_{max} = (1 - \sqrt{\frac{I_0 * R_m}{V}})^2 \tag{7.8}$$

$$\text{Current}_{maxEff} = \sqrt{\frac{V * I_0}{R_m}} \tag{7.9}$$

$$\text{RPM} = K_v * (V - R_m * I) \tag{7.10}$$

Figure 7.5. The winding job is not terrible, but it could have been better.

The general formula for computing a motor's efficiency (7.11) is simply the output power divided by the input power.

$$\text{Efficiency} = \frac{\text{Power}_{out}}{\text{Power}_{in}} = \frac{(V - R_m * I)(I - I_0)}{V * I} \qquad (7.11)$$

You'll probably get the highest overall power system efficiency if you use a motor with a relatively high K_v and a gearbox. But gearboxes cost money and add weight. For most people, using a direct drive outrunner with a low K_v is a good compromise. Keep the current between the point of maximum efficiency and maximum power (7.12).

$$\text{Current}_{maxEff} \leqslant \text{Current}_{target} \leqslant \text{Current}_{maxPower} \qquad (7.12)$$

To help you keep it all straight, here's a quick summary of the symbols used (7.13 on the next page).

$$V = \text{voltage}$$
$$I = \text{current}$$
$$I_0 = \text{no load current} \hspace{2cm} (7.13)$$
$$R_m = \text{internal resistance}$$
$$K_v = \text{voltage constant}$$

7.5. The Problem

It is surprisingly hard to put together an efficient power system for an electric model airplane. Paul Ross (**Ross** 2001) set out to measure the efficiencies of typical electric power systems. He examined 40 electric-powered model airplanes, 36 from magazine reviews. It is safe to assume that the builders that put together these power systems were experienced modelers. Paul calculated the average propeller efficiency at full power was just 39% (max possible is at least 80%).

This is like driving around in your car with the parking brake on. You'll still get there, but your car will have a lot less power available to move you along, not to mention the loss in fuel efficiency. I find this a shocking discovery.

I suppose there is one saving grace in all of this. Our model airplanes (both gas and electric) are so overpowered that we don't even notice when their power systems are serious hobbled. I think most of us could instantly tell the difference between a grossly mis-sized propeller and one that is a good fit. It's just that we are blissfully unaware of the problem in the first place.

7.6. Carlos' Power Rule

Figuring out how much power you need is easy:

"For a sport electric airplane, 10% of the total airplane weight should be the motor and 15% should be the battery. This is valid as long as you use a brushless motor, LiPo batteries, and fly for six minutes."

Carlos' *power rule*

Putting it another way, a motor can handle about 75 watts per ounce of motor weight. You need 75 watts per pound of total airplane weight.

What makes the problem really hard is the flexibility of electric power systems. By the time you consider the battery, motor, gearbox (if any) and propeller, you have an enormous number of combinations. The odds are greatly against finding a good set of power system components.

7.7. Tradeoffs

Picking the right combination of power system components and deciding among all these tradeoffs is what makes it really hard to find an efficient power system for an electric airplane.

Everything else being equal, you want the highest voltage and biggest propeller that you can fit into your model. But it's never this easy. The accompanying tables (see Tables 7.3 to 7.8 on pages 147–149) list some of the trade-offs involved in choosing the components for a power system.

Few Cells	Many Cells
Lower voltage	Higher voltage
Higher current	Lower current
More electric power losses	Fewer electric power losses
May take longer to recharge	May hit # of cells limit in charger

Table 7.3. Battery tradeoffs

Low voltage	High voltage
Easier to find one	HV units are scarce
More power losses	Fewer power losses
More efficient BEC	Usually less efficient BEC

Table 7.4. Speed control tradeoffs

Cool Winding	Hot Winding
Lower voltage constant	Higher voltage constant
Higher torque	Lower torque
Thinner wire	Thicker wire
More windings	Fewer windings
Higher voltage	Lower voltage
Bigger prop	Smaller prop
Lower no load current	Higher no load current
Higher resistance	Lower resistance
Same max power	Same max power
Same weight	Same weight
More efficient	Less efficient

Table 7.5. Motor tradeoffs

Low Gear Ratio	High Gear Ratio
More efficient	Less efficient
Less noise	More noise
no weight penalty	adds weight
no efficiency loss	lowers efficiency

Table 7.6. Gearbox tradeoffs

Small Diameter	Large Diameter
Much less efficient	Much more efficient
Turns faster	Turns slower
More noise	Less noise
Will fit	May not fit
Can fly very fast	Slow airplanes

Table 7.7. Propeller diameter tradeoffs

Low Pitch	High Pitch
better take-off	better high speed
better climb	better cruise
good for slow cruise	good for fast cruise

Table 7.8. Propeller pitch tradeoffs

7.8. Brushless Motors and LiPo Cells

Bob Boucher of Astro Flight wrote a book in 1979 entitled *The Quiet Revolution*. In truth, the electric power revolution did not really occur until much later with the advent of Lithium Polymer (LiPo) cells and brushless motors.

LiPo cells have up to four times the energy density of nickel-cadmium cells, the technology they replaced. A model that previously struggled to fly for five minutes can now cruise along for twenty. That is a big difference.

The main advantages of a brushless motor are durability and flexibility. They can take a lot more abuse. They can also be more efficient, typically about 10% more, but that is not the primary reason why they became popular. Since all outrunner motors are brushless, their popularity nowadays is partly a fortunate accident.

It is sad to see how many introductory electric airplane ready-to-fly (RTF) kits bundle NiCad batteries and cheap brushed motors (see Figure 7.6 on the facing page). I understand the need to keep the entry costs low, but I wonder how many new pilots leave the hobby because they conclude that electric airplanes are not very good flyers.

7.9. Connectors and Wiring

Use appropriately-sized connectors and wiring. It's not too hard for undersized connectors and wiring to have power losses of 20% or more. The determining factor is the current, not the voltage. Even if you cannot feel the heat, it doesn't mean that the power losses are not significant. Use the following table (see Table 7.9 on page 152) to find the right combination for your needs. The given wire sizes are the maximums. You may need to use a slightly smaller wire size due to differences in your specific connector or to make soldering easier.

7.10. Power System Calculators

I do not recommend trying to "eyeball" this one. The chances that you'll get it right are greatly against you.

There are many power system calculators out there, most of them free. Their core functionality is to help you put together an electric power system for a model airplane. Unfortunately, you get what you pay for. I've found the free calculators to be very underpowered (pun intended) and hard to use.

It was my frustration with the available power system calculators that led me to write my own. RCadvisor's EZ Optimizer is the best tool out there for solving this problem. I honestly believe that. It uses advanced artificial intelligence to examine 40,000 component permutations per second. Compare and see for yourself.

Figure 7.6. Friends don't let friends fly with a brushed can motor.

Connector	Max cont	Max wire size	
	current (amps)	gauge	mm²
JST	5	20	0.5
Tamiya	15	17	1.0
Deans Micro	7.5	20	0.5
Anderson PP/Sermos/AMP	30	12	3.3
Multiplex	50	13	2.5
Deans Ultra	60	13	2.5
AstroFlight Zero-Loss	60	13	2.5
1.2 mm bullet	8	20	0.5
1.5 mm bullet	10	20	0.5
3.0 mm bullet	25	15	1.5
4.5 mm bullet	60	13	2.5
5.0 mm bullet	80	13	2.5
7.0 mm bullet	150	11	4.0

Table 7.9. Connectors and wiring

8. Design Process

8.1. The Dangers of Uncertainty

"If God meant for man to fly, he would have made his bones hollow, not his head."

Anonymous

Designing a successful model airplane is mostly a matter of proper planning and managing the risks posed by the unknowns.

Far too many model airplane designers adopt a trial and error approach. Come up with some ideas for changes, build a model, test fly it, repeat. At best you'll get a very subjective feel for which prototype flew better. This is only if you have a great memory and got lucky with identical weather conditions between test flights.

There are two main reasons why this approach fails. First, an airplane is a complex machine to understand. An apparently small change to a design can have several otherwise unrelated consequences to its flight behavior. If your understanding of aircraft design is poor, you'll never sort it all out. Second, there are a huge number of design variables that can be changed. You simply cannot build every design that results from the combination of these variables. So you end up only building a couple of different models, guessing as to what the important variables really are, and guessing at what the right changes should be. If you are lucky, you'll stumble upon a better design. You have no chance of finding the best one.

The opposite approach does not work all that well, either. Don't try to completely design the model on paper and then declare it perfect before you actually build it. The math is just too hard and you'll get bored long before you finish running through all the numbers. Additionally, the difference between theory and practice is always less in theory than it is in practice.

8.2. A Practical Approach

> "If we knew what we were doing, it wouldn't be called research!"
>
> ***Albert Einstein***

Plan on building at least one prototype and throwing it out if you want to end up with a good design. You'll end up doing this anyway, even if you don't plan to!

Study previous designs for ideas and to see what works, but only trust proven designs. Far too many airplane designs (both full-size and models) are fatally flawed, but finding frank discussions of their problems is surprisingly hard. The only folks that really know are the ones that built and flew them, and it does nothing for their reputations or egos to be honest and admit that their airplane is a death trap. Sad but true.

Trust your gut. If it looks right, it probably is. If it doesn't look right, check the numbers again. Show it to others to see what they think. They may not be aircraft designers, but their comments will probably be very insightful. Don't rush the design decisions. That is when you are most likely (as I have) to forget about something.

Do everything possible to isolate the risk areas. It's far better to try out a new construction technique, shaping trick, glue, or material with a throw away test piece before you try it out with a full-blown prototype airplane. I'm always saving scrap pieces of wood or foam and conducting many wacky experiments with them. Some fail miserably, some reveal pleasant surprises. All are interesting and educational.

Try and identify the areas of the design that are probably going to give you trouble. It shouldn't be hard to take a good educated guess at this. It's probably the areas where you are experimenting with new ideas. These are the areas where running the numbers is much more worthwhile. Can you somehow isolate this part of the design to make sure it's working? If you have a radical new wing design, can you build a wing and fly it with a proven fuselage?

Take notes as you go along! I'm a big fan of wide ruled, spiral bound, single subject notebooks. I always have one handy and I'm always using it to take notes about what I'm working on. To help you, I'm including templates for airplane (see Table 8.1 on the following page) and flight (see Table 8.2 on page 157) logs. You are welcome to photocopy these pages for personal use.

When you are building a prototype, keep in mind that it'll have a short lifespan and will likely require repairs and design changes. Don't bother making it pretty. Don't waste time with any decorations. Don't put your best equipment in it. Keep it all inexpensive and expendable. It's okay to take shortcuts when you are building it. A little extra weight or an ugly joint is fine. If possible, make the design modular. Can you swap in a different wing or elevator? It is very hard to predict what you'll want to change down the road, so any modularity built into the design from the beginning is likely to pay off.

8.3. Define Goals

> "The best airplane is the least airplane which will exactly do the job."
>
> *John Thorp*
> *airplane designer*

A well-defined set of requirements are a necessary prerequisite for any successful model airplane design. If you don't know where you are going, how will you know when you get there? It may sound counterintuitive, but having to work within a tight set of constraints is the best way to get the creative juices flowing and is much more likely to lead to innovative solutions than a loose set of requirements.

Name: _____

Manuf: _____   Type: _____

Channel: _____   Tx Mem: _____

Equipment: _____

_____

_____

Notes: _____

_____

_____

Date   **Maintenance Details**

_____   _____

_____   _____

_____   _____

_____   _____

_____   _____

_____   _____

_____   _____

_____   _____

_____   _____

_____   _____

Table 8.1. Airplane log

Name: _____

Date	Flights	Time	Comments
_____	_____	_____	_____
_____	_____	_____	_____
_____	_____	_____	_____
_____	_____	_____	_____
_____	_____	_____	_____
_____	_____	_____	_____
_____	_____	_____	_____
_____	_____	_____	_____
_____	_____	_____	_____
_____	_____	_____	_____
_____	_____	_____	_____
_____	_____	_____	_____
_____	_____	_____	_____
_____	_____	_____	_____
_____	_____	_____	_____
_____	_____	_____	_____
_____	_____	_____	_____

Table 8.2. Flight log

Don't try and come up with the ultimate design the first time out of the gate. That's a recipe for failure. Don't try and introduce too many new ideas in one design. You are bound to get frustrated as you are forced to make numerous design changes to correct too many design flaws. Even worse, problems with the new ideas are bound to interact in nasty ways, making it much more difficult to figure out what the problems really are (yep, the voice of experience talking).

Before you do anything else, think hard about what it is that the design is trying to accomplish. In a worst case scenario, what is the minimum that you will accept before calling the design a success? This better be a very short list!

I'm talking about requirements—what the model must have to be considered a success. The list of desirable features can be a mile long. But it won't be helpful unless you rank them.

8.3.1. Ungoals

Make a list of everything that you don't consider to be important to the success of the design. What is it that you don't care about? Aerobatics? Good looks? Fast speed? Writing these down can be very helpful in sorting out your thoughts about what you are really trying to accomplish. Try it.

8.3.2. Airplane Size

There are various recognized size categories for model airplanes. Giant scale is either 1/4 scale or higher or a wingspan of 80 inches (2 meters) or higher. Park flyers must weigh 2 pounds (1 kilogram) or less. Indoor models are generally 6 ounces (170 grams) or less. Micro R/C aircraft are usually from one to three ounces (28 to 85 grams). Submicro aircraft are less than one ounce.

The military has recently developed an interest in small flying aircraft. According to the Defense Advanced Projects Research Agency (DARPA), a micro air vehicle (MAV) has a maximum linear dimension of six inches (15 centimeters). DARPA funded research into MAVs through 2000, when they concluded that the technology was not advanced enough to meet all of their goals. There are ongoing student MAV competitions which permit a maximum linear dimension of 15 inches (38 centimeters). A recently introduced concept is that of a nano air vehicle which has a span of three inches (7.5 centimeters).

If the model is intended for any kind of competition, make sure you completely understand all of the relevant rules. Not all of the rules are always written down. There are often "unwritten" rules derived from customs and traditions that are just as important. Look carefully at the existing designs. Is there some aspect of their designs that you don't understand? It could be either a design requirement that you overlooked or an area ripe for exploitation.

8.3.3. Materials

Commercial model airplane designs often choose materials for their marketing value or ease of mass manufacturing. Carbon fiber and Depron are just about the two most expensive materials you could use in a model airplane. The price premium for "best" as compared to "good enough" is very high. A well thought-out design made out of wood will be hard to beat under most circumstances.

8.3.4. Construction Difficulty

Is the design buildable by a beginner using simple tools? How many hours will it take them to put it together? Are more advanced materials, such as fiberglass, required? Consider the other requirements first. If it's a trainer, then it is much more likely that a beginner will want to build one. A builder of a gas airplane is more likely to be familiar with balsa construction techniques than with the nuances of a foam design.

8.3.5. Performance

Nothing leads to compromised designs faster than having to meet multiple performance goals. A high climb rate, a fast cruise speed, large cargo-carrying capacity, and long flight duration are all in conflict with each other in some way. For example, one of the ways to get a high climb rate is to make the wing larger, which will hurt your cruise speed. You are allowed to pick one performance goal to optimize. But for everything else it would be very helpful to set specific pass/fail goals.

8.4. Flight Testing

> "There are old pilots, bold pilots, but no old-bold pilots."
>
> ***Anonymous***

Be careful out there. I once tried to make a maiden flight on a new model with the aileron controls reversed. This was after I had checked them *three* times. Oops. I now try and have a friend do a complete "sanity check" before I take a first flight. If you are very nervous, have a friend also do the first flight. Spectators are almost always a bad idea.

The latest generation of in-flight computerized data recorders can come in very handy. They are still a bit heavy to use with indoor models, but otherwise plugging one into a power system is very easy. Having some objective data is very useful. Watch out for sensors that rely on air pressure, since they are hard to calibrate and are prone to measurement errors. If you can afford one, a GPS sensor is a great addition.

How do you know you have a winner on your hands? Or as the case may be, how do you know how much of a loser you have on your hands? Well, years ago NASA developed a scale to help their test pilots answer that question (see Figure 8.1 on the facing page). Don't get hung up on the exact meanings of the numbers. Just be aware of what makes a nice handling airplane and what can get in the way of achieving that goal.

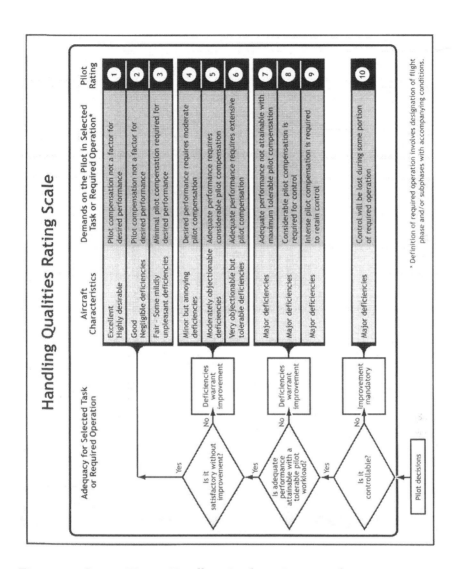

Figure 8.1. Cooper Harper Handling Qualities Rating Scale

8.4.1. Flight Test Plan

"If you have no plan, you have no goal."

Harold Little
Aircraft Manufacturer
1994

Have a good idea what you want to do in each flight **before** you take off (see Figure 8.2 on page 164). Use a checklist (see Table 8.3 on the facing page) to keep track of what still needs to be tested. Pay attention to all the little noises and unexpected movements in the airplane. Trust your instincts. If you think something is wrong, it probably is. Don't second guess yourself—just come in for a landing. Check everything over before you launch again. Above all else, don't forget to always fly your plane. Whatever the problem is, you can deal with it **after** you bring it down safely.

8.4.2. Robustness

"The Laws of Aerodynamics are unforgiving and the ground is hard."

Michael Collins
Astronaut and Test Pilot
1987

I'm not just talking about surviving a crash. I'm also talking about having a design that is resistant to construction or control input mistakes. Pay very close attention when you are building the model and test flying it. Do you see any patterns? Was some construction step substantially harder than the others? What could you do to simplify it? Was a required flight maneuver hard to do? What if the CG is not in quite the right spot. Is the airplane still flyable? Will they still end up with a good airplane, even if they use a slightly different type of foam or wood?

There's a school of though that says that you should lighten any part of the airplane that did *not* break in the last crash. That may be an extreme point

Handling Qualities
- ○ low and high speed taxi
- ○ zero and 50% power stalls
- ○ adverse yaw
- ○ slow flight maneuvering
- ○ control harmony
- ○ slips
- ○ rolls
- ○ inside and outside loops
- ○ inverted flight

Performance
- ○ maximum cruise speed
- ○ maximum climb rate
- ○ maximum roll rate
- ○ power off glide angle
- ○ flight duration at 75% power

Stability
- ○ hands-off level flight
- ○ recovery from disturbed attitude
- ○ spin recovery
- ○ aft and forward CG

Flight Loads
- ○ simulated gusts
- ○ hard landing

Table 8.3. Flight testing checklist

Figure 8.2. Launching a new model
Know what you are going to do *before* you launch.

of view, but I think there's a grain of truth to it. The right question to ask is whether it was reasonable to expect the model to survive the crash. If it was a terrible crash and it did not break, then you need to lighten something up. If it was just a hard landing and it all fell apart, then you need to add more strength somewhere.

8.5. Design Best Practices

Define your goals	Keep it well focused.
Mission first	Forget about design purity.
Not too much innovation	So you can get the bugs out.
Don't sweat the details	Focus first on the overall design.
Keep it simple	Plan to build and throw out a prototype. You will anyway.
Keep it inexpensive	Because you will crash a lot as you get the bugs out.
Keep it clean	Streamline it or eliminate it.
Low weight	Build to fly, not crash. If in doubt, leave it out.
High aspect ratio	For efficient wings.
Thin airfoil	About 5% in the smaller models.
High voltage	Better power efficiency.
Motor 10%	Use a motor that is about 10% of the all-up gross weight.
Battery 15%	Similarly for the battery.
Large propeller	One place where size matters.

8.6. Final Thoughts

"When the bird and the book disagree, always believe the bird."

James Audubon

author

Birds of America

Many so-called "original" airplane designs (models *and* full-size) are really a rehashing of existing designs. There is nothing wrong with doing that on your first design. Just be aware that a world of possibilities await the truly adventurous designer.

I'm always studying other airplane designs to try and learn the thought process that the designer went through. This is a useful exercise that gets easier with practice.

In the best airplane designs, all of their parts work together in harmony to produce a whole that is much greater than their sum. This is not easy to do. Always try and make design decisions that solve multiple design problems at the same time.

Above all else, have fun. Enjoy the process. Share the experience with others. If this book inspires you to design a model airplane, I'd love to hear about it.

Appendices

A. Inexpensive Design Tools

It is too easy to get bogged down trying to learn a CAD program. Most of the time, you don't need one. If you insist, here are some popular choices.

Google SketchUp

`http://sketchup.google.com/`
Free and easy to use 3D editing software. Very popular.

RibbonSoft Qcad

`http://www.qcad.org/`
Nice CAD program. There are paid and free versions. This is what I use myself.

Alibre Design Xpress 3D Solid Modeler

`http://www.alibre.com/xpress/software/`
`alibre-design-xpress.asp`
Free 3D modeling software. Looks impressive.

Siemens Solid Edge 2D Drafting

`http://www.plm.automation.siemens.com/en_us/`
`products/velocity/solidedge/free2d/index.shtml`
I like the price—free.

Upperspace ModelCAD

http: //www. upperspace. com/products/1019/
  A popular CAD program for modelers (not free).

devCAD

http: //www. devcad. com/
  Another popular CAD program for modelers (not free).

Autodesk Design Review

http: //www. autodesk. com/designreview
  Useful for viewing Autodesk's DWF files. Free.

Autodesk Inventor LT

http: //labs. autodesk. com/technologies/inventor_
lt/
  The "light" version of their 3D drawing application (may be free).

IMSI TurboCAD

http: //www. turbocad. com/
  They seem to have a lot of loyal customers (not free).

B. Free On-line Resources

Can you get something for nothing? When it comes to model airplane design information, you can.

On-line Discussion Groups

```
http: //www. rcgroups. com/
http: //www. rcuniverse. com/forum
http: //www. wattflyer. com/
http: //www. slofly. com/
http: //www. rctalk. co. uk/forum/
http: //www. rchangout. com/
```
I have a love-hate relationship with on-line discussion groups. Their posting policies are maddeningly inconsistent. They contain some real gems, but boy, they also contain a lot of silliness! Searching for specific information usually turns into a long frustrating experience. Visit them, but don't believe everything you read there.

Wikipedia

```
http: //www. wikipedia. org/
```
"Use the source, Luke!" A great starting point when you want to understand a subject, *any* subject, better.

Aerospace Web

`http://www.aerospaceweb.org/`

Very authoritative and clear explanations of important aerospace and engineering principles. Not nearly as comprehensive as Wikipedia, but if you want to make sure you have the right answer, look here.

NASA Technical Reports Server

`http://ntrs.nasa.gov/`

An extensive collection of aviation-related research reports. Sometimes tax dollars produce truly outstanding results. This is one of them. The newer reports require a nominal fee.

Model Aviation

`http://www.modelaircraft.org/membersonly.aspx`
`http://www.modelaircraft.org/insider/index.html`

You probably get their great magazine, *Model Aviation*, as part of your AMA membership. Threw out your copy? No problem. Your local library may keep the last two years handy. Need an older issue? Still no problem! The AMA has digitized every issue from 1975 to 2000. To gain access, you need to register at the AMA website using your AMA number. The *AMA Insider* is a free on-line magazine filled with articles originally published in club newsletters. Good stuff.

R/C Modeler

`http://www.rcmmagazine.com/`

This great magazine is no longer being published, but it still lives on the Internet as a free archive. There is a huge amount of information on their website.

Model Airplane News

`http://findarticles.com/p/articles/mi_qa3819`
Many local libraries carry the last two years of this very popular model airplane print publication. Articles two years and older are at FindArticles.com. Their archive goes back to 1997. The only drawback is that graphics from the articles (photos, diagrams, etc) are not included. I discovered that through my Alma Mater I had access to PDF copies of the articles with all the graphics intact. This is worth looking into.

AIAA Design Competition

`http://www.aiaadbf.org/`
Cessna/Raytheon Missile Systems Student Design/Build/Fly competition. Look here for ideas on how to document a design.

R/C Soaring Digest

`http://www.rcsoaringdigest.com/`
Ten years ago I was subscribed to the print edition of this great magazine. The last printed issue was in March 2004. Since then the quality has remained high but the issues are freely downloadable from their website as PDF files. Beautiful photography! Often technical, it is never dull or too hard to understand.

Ampeer

`http://homepage.mac.com/kmyersefo/ampeer.html`
From February 1988 through December 1995, only print copies of the Ampeer existed. It is now a free on-line magazine. A print subscription is still available. Great informational articles for electric enthusiasts.

All Things That Fly

`http: //www. allthingsthatfly. com/`
These are free R/C podcast audio recordings downloadable as MP3 files. Very entertaining and informational.

R/C Flight Cast

`http: //www. rcflightcast. com/`
Another free R/C podcast. They cover different topics than *All Things That Fly*, so keep an eye (ear?) on both.

RCUniverse

`http: //www. rcuniverse. com/magazine/`
RCUniverse also has a free on-line magazine, and they include some feature articles.

The Wing is the Thing

`http: //www. twitt. org/`
Some nice free articles about tailless designs. They also have an inexpensive printed monthly newsletter.

The Nurflügel Page

`http: //www. nurflugel. com/`
Great information about tailless designs.

C. Where to Buy Stuff

Scrounging and finding bargains is a lot of fun. I find myself willingly walking into stores that I'd never gone into before. I walk the aisles trying to come up with uses for some of the strange stuff I see.

Walmart

`http://www.walmart.com/`
Wally world! Great selection and prices. I love walking the aisles looking for ideas. Great selection of plastic containers of all sizes. Inexpensive cutting mats for my worktable. They have the best deal in bamboo sticks, 100 for $1, and they have a larger diameter than other ones I've come across. Not long ago I bought a really inexpensive swivelling desk chair for my worktable. It was a floor sample, so I only paid about $40.

By the way, I've had the air cylinders on two office chairs go bad on me (not purchased at Walmart). In both cases, a quick call to the manufacturers scored me free replacement cylinders. One of the chairs was ten years old! I guess this is what they mean by "hidden warranties".

Harbor Freight

http: //www. harborfreight. com/

Great place to buy tools. Not necessarily top quality, but most of the time they're good enough. Catch them on special, and you'll often pay half or less than half of regular price. Rotary tools and accessories (similar to Dremel), screwdrivers, pliers, tweezers, hand sanders, etc. They have a great digital caliper which I use all the time. Inexpensive 100 packs of X-Acto and razor blades.

Harbor Freight has a program called the Inside Track Club. It only costs like $10/year, so if you buy from them often it's worth it.

Sears Craftsman Club

http: //www. craftsman. com/craftsmanclub/

For a long time I was keeping my eye on a $30 digital angle meter from Harbor Freight. I waited for a while for a good deal on that one. The best that I saw was a discount to $25.

Then one day I got a Sears Craftsman Club sales announcement with a nicer looking digital meter for just $20. Score!

Craftsman tools are pretty high quality, and joining their club is free. Catch the right special, and you'll get a bargain just like me.

Hobby Lobby and Michael's

http: //www. hobbylobby. com/
http: //www. michaels. com/

The craft store, not the hobby store. Great selection of glues, including cyanoacrylates (CA). A good assortment of spruce, balsa and hardwood sticks. They carry the Midwest Cellfoam 88, which is very similar to Depron. You can buy Mylar film for covering models. A huge assortment of stickers for decorating models. A large selection of X-Acto knives and blades. Velcro for sticking down batteries and receivers.

Don't pay full price! Sign up for their mailing list. Once a week they send out an email with specials. If you are lucky, they'll have in there a 40% off any one item coupon. I happen to have two stores near me, so it's easy to combine a trip there with something else I'm doing.

Michael's is very similar to Hobby Lobby. Their coupons are for 50% off any one item. Their coupons don't come as often and their selection is not as good, so I don't usually shop there.

Dollar Tree

http://www.dollartree.com/

Home of the dollar foamboard and the dollar rubbing alcohol. I sometimes get a dollar candy bag while I'm there. Otherwise, I don't recall ever buying anything else there. Most of the time you can find better deals at Walmart.

Lowe's and Home Depot

http://www.lowes.com/
http://www.homedepot.com/

I got a solid wood door there for something like $50 that I use as my worktable. I put about five coats of boat varnish on it. It looks great! They carry Dow Styrofoam (blue). Great selection of industrial adhesives.

Home Depot carries a similar selection to Lowe's. Their foam is from Owens Corning (pink). The blue stuff is better.

Hobby King

http: //www. hobbyking. com/

They used to be called Hobby City and are located in Hong Kong. I believe that their parent company is called United Hobbies, and they also sell branded products that they manufacture, such as Turnigy. Very inexpensive! Servos, motors, batteries, building supplies, etc.

A couple of caveats. First, unless you are willing to pay a premium on the shipping (which kind of defeats the purpose of shopping from them), the stuff takes a long time to show up. Don't start looking for it until three weeks after you placed the order.

Second, good luck trying to return an item. I'm not saying that they don't honor the product warranties. It's just that communicating with their Hong Kong office is challenging and sending something back can get expensive. I've never had a problem with anything I've ordered from them, but if something shows up defective I'll probably just chuck it and order another one.

Glossary

advance ratio Relates a propeller's airspeed with the rotational frequency and diameter. It is closely related to the angle of attack of the propeller blades.

aerodynamic stall The sudden reduction in lift of an airfoil as the angle of attack is increased. For most airfoils this occurs at about 15 degrees. Note that airspeed is only indirectly responsible for stalls.

air density ratio The ratio of the current air density to that of standard conditions at sea level.

airfoil The cross-sectional shape of a wing, propeller, or stabilizer.

airspeed The speed of movement relative to the air.

angle of attack The angle between the chord line of an airfoil and the relative wind. Note that, for most non-symmetrical airfoils, even if the angle of attack is zero lift will still be generated.

aspect ratio The ratio of a wing's span to its average chord length. A value of six is common.

camber The difference in shape between the upper and lower surfaces of an airfoil. Symmetrical airfoils have no camber.

chord The length of the chord line of an airfoil.

chord line A straight line connecting the leading edge and the trailing edge of an airfoil.

component One of several different entities that the RCadvisor calculator is designed to edit. Motors, propellers, airfoils, etc.

density altitude The equivalent altitude above sea level when temperature effects are taken into account. It can have a profound effect on the efficiency of wings and propellers.

drag coefficient A dimensionless quantity characterizing the drag produced by an airfoil.

efficiency The ability to produce useful work from a given unit of energy. Wasted energy is usually turned into heat, sound, or light. Efficiency is a dimensionless quantity.

electrical current The amount of electric charge moving through a medium. Usually measured in amperes. A useful analogy is to think of a water hose. Current is like the amount of water moving through the hose. The higher the current, the higher the electrical resistance and corresponding efficiency losses.

electrical resistance The degree to which a material opposes the movement of an electric current. Measured in ohms. The wasted energy is normally converted into heat.

electronic speed control Works similar to a throttle on a gas engine. It electronically lowers the voltage seen by the motor in order to control its rotational frequency. Nowadays they are all pretty efficient.

energy The ability to do work. It is a scalar quantity (in other words, it does not specify a direction). It is closely related to torque, which is rotational force. Common units are the joule, kilowatt-hour and foot-pound.

gearbox A gearing mechanism for reducing the RPMs while increasing the torque of a motor. A gearbox permits the use of much more efficient larger diameter propellers at some small cost in overall efficiency and weight.

Hertz Cycles per second. A unit of frequency.

inrunner An inrunner is a traditional style motor where the core rotates and the outside can is stationary. The opposite of an outrunner.

internal resistance The power losses in an electrical component. Typically manifested as heat.

lift coefficient A dimensionless quantity characterizing the lifting force produced by an airfoil.

Mach number A dimensionless quantity measuring a speed relative to the speed of sound. It is about 750 mi/h (350 m/s). As an airfoil approaches Mach 1, both its lift and drag increase dramatically.

maximum airfoil thickness The maximum thickness of an airfoil expressed as a percentage of the chord.

mean camber line A line drawn from the leading edge of an airfoil to its trailing edge equidistant from the upper and lower surfaces. The line will be curved except on a symmetrical airfoil.

motor Motors are electric; engines are internal combustion. Cheap motors in toys are inrunners that use ferrite magnets. The input voltage determines the RPMs and the input electric current the torque. The motors that we use have a linear relationship between torque and RPM for a given voltage. Maximum torque occurs at zero RPM and results in maximum electric current being drawn. Maximum RPM occurs when there is no load on the shaft. The power produced by a motor is the product of the RPMs and the torque.

n100W RPM of the propeller when it is absorbing 100 watts of power. Defined to be measured at zero airspeed and standard atmospheric conditions. Note that this is not the power going into the motor, but the power available to the propeller.

n10N RPM of the propeller when it is generating 10 newtons of static thrust. This is about 2.25 pounds of force. Defined to be measured at zero airspeed and standard atmospheric conditions.

no load current The electrical current drawn by a motor when the output shaft is allowed to rotate freely. Below this current level, the motor will not turn. Normally measured at 10 volts, sometimes at 8. In theory, this quantity is not dependent on the input voltage. In reality, inexpensive motors require higher current for higher voltages.

outrunner In an outrunner electric motor, the core with the windings stays stationary and the outside can with the magnets spins. The opposite of an inrunner.

power Energy per unit of time. Common units include the watt (one joule of energy per second) and horsepower (550 foot-pounds of energy per second).

power-speed coefficient Relates the forward velocity with the power required to turn a propeller. It is closely related to a propeller's efficiency. It is sometimes used to help determine the correct propeller diameter to use.

propeller An airscrew. Ultimately, it is the thrust produced by the propeller that counts. Every other power system component is there in a supporting role. The bigger the diameter, the better.

propeller diameter Twice the distance from a propeller tip to the center of the hub. This should be as big as possible in order to maximize the propeller efficiency.

propeller pitch The distance that a propeller would move forward in one complete revolution if moving through a solid. If the pitch is too high, then the propeller will be stalled if the forward motion is too low. Some propellers are stalled at the beginning of the take-off run. On the other hand, high pitch is needed for fast moving models such as pylon racers.

Reynolds number A dimensionless quantity characterizing the dynamic behavior of a fluid. It is determined by the viscosity of the fluid, the velocity of the flow, and the size of the object.

rotational frequency How quickly something rotates. Think Hertz (cycles per second), not mi/h.

RPM Revolutions per minute.

torque Rotational or angular force. It is a pseudo-vector quantity. The units are the same as for energy: newton-meter and foot-pound. Joules are not used to measure torque.

torque constant Relates a motor's input current with the available torque.

voltage The difference in electrical potential energy between two points. A useful analogy is to think of a water hose. Voltage is like the speed of the water moving through the hose. Measured in volts.

voltage constant Relates the rotational frequency of the motor to the input voltage. Net input voltage $*$ voltage constant = RPM.

Watt Unit of electrical power. 750 watts is about one horsepower.

zero lift angle Non-symmetrical airfoils still generate lift even if their angle of attack is zero. The negative angle at which they generate no lift is called the zero lift angle. For most airfoils this is about -3 degrees, but it is very dependent on the Reynolds number and the exact shape of the airfoil. Its normal range is -5 to 0 degrees.

Annotated Bibliography

Printed books were invented five and a half centuries ago. Before that time it would take a skilled craftsman a year to make one copy of a single book. Today there are two and a half billion books sold each year.

I own copies of every book listed in this bibliography. I have learned something from all of them. Rather than just providing a simple list, I've added frank comments based on my impressions of each book. Hopefully your curiosity will lead you to obtain copies of one or more of these books so that you may continue your education.

I also own a filing cabinet full of printed technical reports, but it's simply not practical to list them here. NACA, NASA, and the recent MAV (micro air vehicle) researchers are fantastic sources of information, almost all of it freely available over the Internet.

Highly Recommended

Hoadley, **R. Bruce** (2000). *Understanding Wood.* Taunton Press. A classic. Almost qualifies as a coffee table book. It's full of beautiful pictures and illustrations. Don't let them fool you. There's a ton of great technical information about wood and how to work with it.

Lambie, **Jack** (1987). *Designing and Building Composite R/C Model Aircraft.* Motorbooks International. A great but little known book. Full of practical advice and ideas. The book covers mostly composite construction and aerodynamics. If you find an inexpensive copy, snap it up.

Lennon, Andy (1996). *Basics of R/C Model Aircraft Design.* Air Age Media. Andy Lennon wrote two similar model airplane books. This one is large format and full of pictures and illustrations. The other book is smaller and older. In some ways the earlier book feels like a first edition of this one. This book gets straight to the point and I consult it often for guidance.

Mises, Richard Von (1959). *Theory of Flight.* Dover Publications. I love this book! Inexpensive, jam packed full of information, easy to read, no calculus, lots of useful formulas and diagrams. What's not to like? A must have.

Raymer, Daniel P. (2006). *Aircraft Design: A Conceptual Approach.* 4th ed. American Institute of Aeronautics and Astronautics. Wow. If you've ever wondered how a real airplane gets designed, then read this book. It is written by a master in his field. Not inexpensive, but one of my most often used technical references. If I read something in the book, I know Mr. Raymer learned it through years of hard experience.

Simons, Martin (2002). *Model Aircraft Aerodynamics.* 4th ed. Special Interest Model Books. Up to edition 4, and it shows. Lots of information about model airplane aerodynamics. It's almost all qualitative, though. The few equations included are in an appendix. But it's great for understanding how all the design trade-offs work together. Pretty easy to read, too.

Aircraft Design

Aird, Forbes (2006). *Fiberglass & Other Composite Materials.* HPBooks. A great introduction to composite construction. Not too technical. If you've been wondering what's the big deal about using carbon fiber, read this book. It'll be an eye opener.

Anderson, John D. (1999). *Aircraft Performance and Design.* McGraw-Hill. Not as popular as the other Anderson books. Lots of equations for estimating the performance of an airplane. There is nothing wrong with the book, but I tend to consult my other references more.

Askue, **Vaughan** (1992). *Flight Testing Homebuilt Aircraft.* Iowa State University Press. Much more broader in scope than Smith's book. Covers a whole host of modifications that can be made to an aircraft to cure bad behavior. Want to know what vortilons are used for? Read this book.

Chevalier, **Howard** (1993). *Model Airplane Design and Performance for the Modeler.* Challenge Engineering. Covers similar ground to the Lennon books. Has enough formulas to let you compute the values for your own model. Don't let all the numbers scare you. If you are willing to do the calculations, this book will take you there.

Foreman, **Cindy** (2002). *Advanced Composites.* Jeppesen Sanderson. More advanced and more technical than Aird's book. Gets into a lot of nitty gritty of working with these materials. A good second book to read on the subject.

Gale, **Dr. Ing. Ferdinando** (1993). *Structural Dimensioning of Radioguided Aeromodels, A Manual for Aeromodelers.* B2Streamlines. A rare book whose entire focus is model airplane structural design. A lot harder to read than it needed to be, but still very useful.

Grant, **Charles Hampson** (1941). *Model Airplane Design and Theory of Flight.* Jay Publishing. A book that shouldn't exist. Published in 1941, it is very professionally written and typeset. Every other model airplane book from that era looks homemade by comparison. A comprehensive 500 page look at model airplane design and construction by the co-founder of the Academy of Model Aeronautics. I found a used copy years ago and I consider myself very lucky to own one.

– (1983). *Aero Science of Free Flight.* Sharp Offset Printing Inc. I had never heard of this book until I found a copy! The second edition of his earlier work. A beautiful book, it again weighs in at over 500 pages. You can still find inexpensive used copies of this excellent book.

Hibbeler, **R. C.** (2004). *Statics & Dynamics.* 10th ed. Pearson Prentice Hall. A big and heavy college textbook. More than you ever wanted to know about computing the physical loads on all sorts of structures. I found it easy to follow. The numerous full-color illustrations helped.

Hoffman, R.J. (1955). *Model Aeronautics made Painless.* Model Aeronautic Publications. A serious model airplane design book by a very experienced full-size airplane designer. Some pages are written by hand. All pages are packed full of information. If you come across an inexpensive copy, buy it.

Lennon, Andy (1986). *R/C Model Airplane Design.* Motorbooks International. Andy Lennon is my favorite model airplane book author. He has a fantastic can-do attitude that I wish more folks had. He never shied away from an unusual design. Every page of his books seems to be shouting out: you can do it! His two books have a lot of overlap in subject area. I like his newer book better since it's more approachable.

Newman, Jim (1987). *400 Great R/C Modeling Tips.* Ed. by **Art Schroeder**. Vol. I. Air Age. Though focused on gas airplanes, this is a useful collection of tips. I got an inexpensive secondhand copy.

– (1991). *400 Great R/C Modeling Tips.* Ed. by **Tom Atwood**. Vol. II. Air Age. Volume 2 of the collection of tips. Like the other volume, mainly useful for gas models. Lots of good tips, but you should be able to find a used copy somewhere.

Niles, Alfred S. and **Joseph S. Newell** (1943*a*). *Airplane Structures.* 3rd ed. Vol. 1. John Wiley & Sons. Not intended for casual readers. A scary amount of math in places. Lots of descriptive text, though. The book to read when you really need to design an airplane and want to know exactly the stresses that it will have.

– (1943*b*). *Airplane Structures.* 3rd ed. Vol. 2. John Wiley & Sons. A continuation of volume 1. This volume covers more advanced structures.

Perkins, Courtland and **Robert Hage** (1949). *Airplane Performance Stability and Control.* John Wiley & Sons. Still considered to be an authoritative reference. Contains differential calculus. Not for the faint of heart. Not for beginners. Need I say more?

Randolph, Randy (1991). *R/C Airplane Building Techniques.* Air Age Publishing. Intended for beginners, this book is getting a little dated but is still very useful. It is full of explanations of techniques for solving common model airplane building problems. Lots and lots of photos cover every step along the way. I promise you won't get lost.

Raymer, Daniel P. (2003). *Simplified Aircraft Design for Homebuilders.* Design Dimension Press. I think of this as the 'baby' edition of Raymer's much longer book on a similar subject. It has far fewer pages and a much lower price. Focusing on homebuilt airplanes, it avoids most of the math of its big brother. I like his other book much better, but this one is a good compromise for a lot of people.

Reed, Miles et al. (2005). *IMAA Giant Scale Handbook.* Ed. by **Taylor Collins.** International Miniature Aircraft Association. This is a funny book. The first six pages are all advertisements. There are engine and servo directories of questionable value. The book consists mostly of self-contained articles by different authors. On the other hand, the articles are excellent. Great information, most of which I haven't seen elsewhere.

Shacklock, Kelvin (2007). *Aircraft Workshop: Learn to Make Models that Fly.* Special Interest Model Books. This is a fantastic book. Jam packed full of information, pictures and illustrations. It is not very well known, but it deserves better. Much better. I love the beautifully detailed plans throughout the book. A keeper.

Smith, Hubert (1982). *Performance Flight Testing.* Tab Books. Written for full-size airplane homebuilders. Most of the information in the book can be applied to model airplanes by using the new onboard data loggers. This is an area that most of us know very little about.

Sparks, Keith (2004). *Building with Foam.* Park Flyer Plastics. I liked this book. Not a huge number of pages, but a lot of practical advice on how to make model airplanes out of foam. The author's models are pictured on the back cover and they look amazing.

Strasser, Ben, ed. (1985). *For What It's Worth.* Vol. V. R/C Modeler. A collection of articles from R/C Modeler magazine (no longer in publication). Packed full of information. I bought an inexpensive copy at a club flea market.

– ed. (1988). *For What It's Worth.* Vol. VI. R/C Modeler. Very similar to their other volume.

Thomas, David (1999). *Radio Control Foam Modeling.* Revised. Nexus Special Interests. A really great how-to book. Not so much for indoor or park flyers, but for larger models. Lots and lots of techniques that I guarantee will get your creative juices flowing. Recommended.

Uravitch, Rich (1991). *Scratch-Building R/C Airplanes.* Air Age Publishing. Thin, only about 70 pages long, but informative. More useful to first-time scratchbuilders. Lots of photos. Surprisingly comprehensive, though its coverage of the different subjects is brief.

Warner, Edward P. (1936). *Airplane Design: Performance.* 2nd ed. McGraw-Hill. I get the feeling that this book is the second edition of the other Warner book (listed under Aerodynamics). It is similar in style to his other book, with lots of long descriptive narrative explanations.

Weiss, Alex (1996). *R/C Sports Aircraft from Scratch.* Nexus Special Interests. Another great British book about model airplane design and construction. No math, but lots of great diagrams. Lots of tips and explanations why a given design element works better than another. A good explanation of flutter.

Williams, Ron (2008). *Building & Flying Indoor Model Airplanes.* Necessary Equipment. Originally published in 1984. The 2008 edition is a reprint. Considered the bible of indoor model airplane construction. Includes plans for and covers the construction details of a series of progressively more sophisticated indoor designs. Some of the information is out of date, but the bulk of it is not. Does not cover radio controlled models.

Wilson, R. C. (1941). *Preliminary Airplane Design.* Pitman Publishing Corporation. Short and sweet! Only about 75 pages long. A very practical step-by-step guide to full-size airplane design. Similar to Rayner's books, but not as up to date and a lot less expensive.

Aerodynamics

Abbott, Ira H. and **Albert E. Von Doenhoff** (1959). *Theory of Wing Sections.* Dover Publications. A classic. Dover books are bargains, too. A great reference to the classic NACA airfoil sections. A lot of information on how the shape of the airfoil affects its performance characteristics.

Anderson, **John D**. (2005). *Introduction to Flight*. 5th ed. McGraw-Hill. Probably the most interesting and comprehensive introduction to basic aerodynamics. Lots of historical anecdotes. The focus is more on understanding than in raw equations. Not inexpensive, but a great value.

– (2007). *Fundamentals of Aerodynamics*. 4th ed. McGraw-Hill. Anderson has a great writing style that I find very readable. He loves to add historical anecdotes, which really helps put what he is discussing into context. This is an advanced text, dealing with the intricacies of fluid dynamics. Not for the faint of heart. Not inexpensive.

Ashley, **Holt** and **Marten Landahl** (1985). *Aerodynamics of Wings and Bodies*. Dover Publications. Inexpensive (Penguin), but very advanced mathematically. Unless you like solving advanced calculus problems for fun in your spare time, I'd give this one a wide berth.

Diehl, **Walter Stuart** (1936). *Engineering Aerodynamics*. Revised. Ronald Press. A long book, it contains lots of charts with airplane test data. I find it fascinating to look back in time to see the already advanced state of aerodynamics, just 30 years after the dawn of aviation.

Dwinnell, **James H**. (1949). *Principles of Aerodynamics*. McGraw-Hill. This book is still just as good as a modern book such as those by Anderson. Heck of a lot less expensive, too. Most of the math is straightforward. I refer to this one once in a while.

Hemke, **Paul E**. (1946). *Elementary Applied Aerodynamics*. Prentice-Hall. More approachable than most. Lots of worked out examples. Lots of math but the equations are not overwhelmingly difficult to figure out.

Jones, **Bradley** (1950). *Elements of Practical Aerodynamics*. 4th ed. John Wiley & Sons. The fact that this book made it to its fourth edition is a good sign. Great explanations throughout and the equations do not overwhelm the reader. If you find an inexpensive copy, buy it. This is one of the better ones.

Kuethe, **Arnold M**. and **Chuen-Yen Chow** (1998). *Foundations of Aerodynamics*. 5th ed. John Wiley & Sons. Not inexpensive but very well respected by the aircraft design industry. If you want to understand how XFoil really works, this is the book. The authors cover a lot of ground.

Millikan, **Clark B.** (1941). *Aerodynamics of the Airplane.* John Wiley & Sons. A relatively small book with lots of math equations. Not as approachable as some of the other books from this era.

Phillips, **Warren F.** (2004). *Mechanics of Flight.* John Wiley & Sons. This is one of those rare books that is so good that I never have to question what I read there. It's very, very authoritative. Lots of coverage of the dynamics of flight. Read Anderson for the entertaining anecdotes. Read Phillips for just the facts, ma'am.

Warner, **Edward P.** (1927). *Airplane Design: Aerodynamics.* 1st ed. McGraw-Hill. A big book, but surprisingly few formulas. It consists mostly of narrative explanations of the aerodynamic effects. I guess the formulas were still being developed.

Wood, **Karl D.** (1947). *Technical Aerodynamics.* 2nd ed. McGraw-Hill. This is a nice book. I refer to it once in a while. Lots of appendices with a lot of airfoil data. If you find an inexpensive copy, don't hesitate to snap it up.

Zaic, **Frank** (1987). *Circular Airflow and Model Aircraft.* Revised. Model Aeronautic Publications. Considered a classic. Originally published in 1964. Republished with an addendum in 1987. A fascinating old-fashioned book filled with hand-drawn illustrations and charts. Some of the thinking in the book has become outdated, but it is still a useful reference.

Aerodynamics History

Anderson, **John D.** (1998). *A History of Aerodynamics.* Cambridge University Press. Anderson's forte is the history of aviation, and this book did not disappoint. Much more than just a recounting of the history, Anderson ties the stories into a cohesive narrative that covers an important topic in the history of aviation. The book gave me a great appreciation of the challenges faced by the aviation pioneers.

Karman, Theodore Von (2004). *Aerodynamics, Selected Topics in the Light of Their Historical Development.* Dover Publications. Surprisingly readable. The author is a famous early aerodynamicist, so he lends an authentic air to the discussions. Similar in spirit to the Anderson book, but much less expensive.

Propellers

Brooks, Donald W. (1997). *Prop Talk: Understanding and Optimizing Propeller Performance for Model Electric Aircraft.* ARPI. Covers similar ground to the Chevalier book, but has a much more pragmatic approach. Contains some excellent test data and practical advice. If you are serious about improving the performance of your propellers, then you need this book.

Chevalier, Howard L. (1997). *Model Airplane Propellers, Selection and Performance for the Modeler.* Challenge Engineering. A solid introduction to the aerodynamics of model airplane propellers. Don't be put off by the black and white drawings and all the equations. The book is quite approachable.

Falk, Karl Hansson (1943). *Aircraft Propeller Handbook.* 2nd ed. Ronald Press. A surprisingly technical book from a propeller designer at Hamilton Standard Propellers. Lots of integrals and charts. Designed to be a practical guide to understanding propellers.

Sherlock, Stuart L. (1994). *Propeller Dynamics, Qualitative Fundamentals.* Vol. 1. Stuart L. Sherlock. Self-published by the founder of Supercool Racing Propellers in western Australia. A very readable guide to model airplane propellers, including their design. Surprisingly good, though it's only about 60 pages.

Sailplanes

Gale, Dr. Ing. Ferdinando (1996). *Aerodynamic Design of Radioguided Sailplanes*. B2Streamlines. Don't let the title fool you. The bulk of what's in this book applies to all model airplanes. Lots and lots of information. If you are into designing model gliders, this is a must have.

Hall, Stan (1997). *The Collected Works of Stan Hall*. Ed. by **Janice Hagen** and **Dan Armstrong**. Vol. 1. Sailplane Homebuilders Association. A huge collection of articles by a full-size glider homebuilder. He touches on every technical subject imaginable that is related to building your own glider. Much of it applies directly to models. This is a real treasure trove of information.

– (2003). *The Collected Works of Stan Hall*. Ed. by **Bill Doddman**. Vol. 2. Sailplane Homebuilders Association. Volume 2 of a huge collection of articles by a full-size glider homebuilder.

Reichmann, Helmut (1993). *Cross-Country Soaring*. Revised. Soaring Society of America. A classic guide to full-size glider competition flying. A surprisingly large amount of the material applies just as well to model gliders. Great explanations of many related topics.

Stokely, Herk, ed. (1992). *Soar Tech Journal for Radio Controlled Soaring*. Vol. 9. Soartech. A collection of technical articles about model gliders. Very high quality material. Includes an article by Michael Selig. Another one talks about a 30 foot (10 meter) span paper airplane. Very interesting.

– ed. (1993). *Soar Tech Journal for Radio Controlled Soaring*. Vol. 10. Soartech. A collection of technical articles about model gliders. Very high quality material. Includes a molded glider construction article with lots of pictures. Marred by a large collection of obsolete computer program listings.

Thomas, Fred (1999). *Fundamentals of Sailplane Design*. College Park Press. Translated by Judah Milgram. Full-size glider design book that applies just as well to model gliders. Great appendix with technical data on a huge number of full-size gliders.

Thornburg, Dave (1993). *Old Buzzard's Soaring Book.* 2nd ed. Pony X Press. By the designer of the Bird of Time model glider. A joy to read. Jam packed full of tips on how to design, build and fly model gliders. Highly recommended if you have any interest in this type of model.

Zaic, Frank (1944). *Model Glider Design.* Model Aeronautic Publications. Tons of information about early free flight gliders. The pictures are priceless. About a third of the book is a large collection of classic glider plans.It's amazing to see how advanced they were in their designs and flying techniques.

Tailless

Gale, Dr. Ing. Ferdinando (1991). *Tailless Tale.* B2Streamlines. There are very few technical books that have been published on tailless aircraft, either full-size or models. This is an excellent book whose focus is on tailless model airplanes. There's a lot of information here that cannot be found anywhere else.

Kuhlman, Bill & Bunny (1993). *On the Wing... the book.* Vol. 1. B2Streamlines. A collection of articles from their monthly column on R/C Soaring Digest magazine. The focus is tailless model gliders. There is a ton of information here on this fascinating subject.

– (1997). *On the Wing... the book.* Vol. 2. B2Streamlines. Their second collection of articles from their monthly column on R/C Soaring Digest magazine. The focus is tailless model gliders. There is a ton of information here on this fascinating subject.

Scale

Bowers, Peter M. (1991). *Scale Aircraft Drawings, World War II.* Vol. 2. Air Age Publishing. An incredible amount of information on World War II airplanes. Includes historical background, technical data and scale drawings showing the internal configurations. Very handy. By the designer of the famous Fly Baby homebuilt airplane. Volume I covers World War I aircraft.

Power Systems

Boucher, Robert J. (1979). *The Quiet Revolution*. Astro Flight. A very early electric model airplane guide by a true pioneer in the field. Much of the information is surprisingly still accurate. We have come a long way, baby!

Gierke, David (1994). *2-Stroke Glow Engines for R/C Aircraft*. Vol. 1. Air Age Media. An A-Z guide to model airplane gas engines. This one is in black and white. Gierke's other engine book is in full color. Lots of information on running and maintaining these engines. Lots of historical information.

– (2005). *Radio Control Airplane Engine Guide*. Air Age Media. Comprehensive guide to selecting, running and maintaining gas engines. Full color. Think of it as volume 2 of his earlier work, since they have little overlap. Curiously, his earlier book had an index while this one doesn't.

Nadler, Bob (2008). *Electric RC Flying for Cheapskates*. f/22 Press. Hmmm. Fairly short. Great information on putting together an inexpensive beginner's electric airplane package. Good links to source of inexpensive R/C stuff. However, I didn't get as much out of this as I had hoped.

Ross, Paul (2001). *Sizing Electric Power for your Model Airplane*. Tech. rep. Self Published. URL: `http://home.att.net/~pfrswr/sizing.htm`. A ground-breaking work by a very methodical individual. A real eye opener to see how inefficient electric power systems are in actual practice.

Index

Colophon

About the Author

I founded RCadvisor.com in 2007. Born in Puerto Rico, I grew up in New York City.

I've had life-long love affairs with airplanes and computers. As a child, I built and flew many rubber-powered model airplanes. I then moved on to small gas control-line models. In the mid-90s I helped pioneer the electric revolution by flying a .40 size electric model. I hold a Private Pilot-Glider license and once owned a full-size AS-W 20 high performance sailplane. I'm currently very active in my local model airplane clubs, recently accepting the position of Vice President at one of them.

I bought my first personal computer in 1981 and got my first paying job as a computer programmer in 1983. I received a degree in Computer Science from Columbia University and have extensive experience in the field.

RCadvisor's Calculator

Some of the website visitors are very curious about the story behind the calculator. Here is a summary of that story.

I've been a computer programmer all my life. I got my first personal computer in 1980 and got my first paid job as a computer programmer a couple of years later while still in high school. I've also been a fan of aviation for as long as I can recall. While growing up, I always dreamed of becoming an airline pilot. I've been straddling these two fields my entire life.

During the summer of 2007 I was putting together an electric power system for a new model airplane I had just purchased. I was very disappointed

Figure C.1. Carlos Reyes

with the power system calculators available. It looked like the time was right for a shake-up in the model airplane calculator market. I've been working on it full-time since then. I don't have much time to go flying right now!

I wrote the first version of the calculator using Dojo[1], a web browser AJAX toolkit which uses JavaScript. I liked how it was coming together, but ran into a problem when it came time to do the charts. You see, there are no good solutions for doing interactive graphics from JavaScript today. The best solution I found was a Flash chart control. It worked fine, but then I started thinking. Why not do the whole application using Flash?

I finally settled on Adobe Flex[2], a very powerful application framework. Flex is compiled and runs inside Flash. It looks great (see Figure C.2 on the next page)! I'm only using the open source core of Flex. Ironically, I ended up writing my own charting module. The calculator was at about 26,000 lines of source code the last time I checked. Flex is a very high-level computer programming language, so that actually is a lot of source code.

---

[1] www.dojotoolkit.org
[2] www.adobe.com/flex

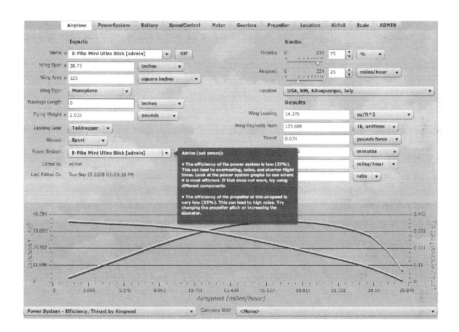

Figure C.2. RCadvisor's calculator

Website

It sounds funny to me now, but my original plan was to keep the website around the calculator as minimal as possible. Similar to Google's[3] landing page, it was going to consist of not much more than the calculator. About a week before the official launch on January 1, 2008, I decided that the calculator merited a full-blown website.

The web server runs Drupal[4], a great open source content management system. I've customized it with about fifty add-on modules and much elbow grease.

This Book

This is my first published book. I decided to do all the work myself. I wrote it using LaTeX, an incredibly powerful open source document processing system with an equally massive learning curve. The entire book is just one large plain text file of about 6,500 lines with the contents and all the LaTeX commands all mixed in together.

As you can probably guess, I'm a big fan of open source software. I've been running Linux[5] as the primary operating system on my desktop for several years now.

Regrets? Never.

---

[3] www.google.com
[4] www.drupal.org
[5] www.linux.org

Made in the USA
San Bernardino, CA
02 December 2016